Pr

Sustainable Content

"This book transformed the way I advise clients to consider the impact of 'just-in-case' content. Instead of narrowly focusing on UX and internal resources to manage content, we can now put hard numbers to the greater cost to the environment. Alisa's case for sustainable content isn't just about best practices. It's about empowering ourselves as professional communicators to advocate for responsible use of resources far beyond the short-term impact we're used to focusing on."

—**Kristina Halvorson**, CEO of Brain Traffic and
author of *Content Strategy for the Web*

"Storing unlimited globs of content on the internet could never be cost-free, but it's been hard to pinpoint what to measure. Now, Alisa Bonsignore has done the math for us. With *Sustainable Content*, we can make data-driven decisions to save the world while using content wisely."

—**Torrey Podmajersky**, president of Catbird Content and
author of *Strategic Writing for UX*

"In addressing the environmental impact of creating and transferring and storing digital content, Alisa uncovers not necessarily another problem but another solution we can all drive toward as we look to create sustainability in our own lives, in our communities, and on our planet. What's more, as she outlines the ways we can reduce our content footprint, she provides a template for more effective and efficient communication—full stop. (Not to mention, she creates a compelling argument for keeping your video off on your next Zoom.)"

—**Melanie Mannarino**, author of
The (Almost) Zero Waste Guide

"When I moved from print journalism to digital content, I thought that, because was pushing pixels instead of paper, I was doing my part to help reduce waste and its negative impact on the environment—something I'd embraced in my personal life as well. I couldn't have been more wrong. Well, maybe not *wrong* but certainly misguided. As it turns out—and as Bonsignore writes in her book—'Moving data requires energy.' Apparently, I wasn't quite making the impact that I thought I was.

Thankfully, many of the best practices embraced by digital content creators—like using plain language and doing more with less—puts us in a prime position to use everyday tools to help lead sustainability efforts. This book will help you understand the ecological costs of digital content and its impact on sustainability. It will teach you how to measure the footprint of digital content while considering the impact of AI and the ROI of sustainable content. And, perhaps most importantly, Bonsignore helps us see how the content we create—and the best practices used to create it—can be both useful and sustainable."

—**Natalie Marie Dunbar**, CEO of the Content Practice
Architect and author of *From Solo to Scaled:
Building a Sustainable Content Strategy Practice*

"It's been more than 30 years since Mike Markel first asserted that all employees, including technical communicators and content experts, have an ethical obligation to support the environment by limiting use of energy and natural resources in their work. Since then, however, relatively little has been written about the environmental costs of technical and professional communication. Bonsignore's book explains the issues clearly and shows that computing the environmental costs of our work is not only feasible but ethically necessary. Bonsignore shows that while climate change is the most wicked of problems, creating content sustainably is an ethical and financially beneficial response."

—**Russell Willerton**, PhD, author of *Plain Language
and Ethical Action: A Dialogic Approach to
Technical Content in the Twenty-First Century*

Sustainable Content

How to Measure and Mitigate

the Carbon Footprint

of Digital Data

Alisa Bonsignore

RIVER GROVE
BOOKS

Published by River Grove Books
Austin, TX
www.rivergrovebooks.com

Distributed by River Grove Books

Design and composition by Greenleaf Book Group
Cover design by Greenleaf Book Group and Adrian Morgan
Cover image used under license from © malp | Adobe Stock

Publisher's Cataloging-in-Publication data is available.

Print ISBN: 978-1-63299-882-8

eBook ISBN: 978-1-63299-883-5

First Edition

For Evan

Contents

Introduction

"Don't panic." It's the first helpful or intelligible
thing anybody's said to me all day.

—**ARTHUR DENT,** *The Hitchhiker's Guide to the Galaxy*

THE ROOTS OF THIS BOOK go way, way back to the last century:
the 1990s. The public attention to environmental topics focused
on the ozone layer, recycling, and activists chaining themselves
to trees to prevent logging. For those of us who came of professional age alongside the newfangled technology known as the
World Wide Web, digital was the be-all, end-all of innovation and
progress. Digital was the future! We were going to have paperless
offices! There was no reason to kill trees for paper (such a terrible,
primitive idea). We spoke of this paperless future like a shiny sci-fi
utopia. After all, digital was free and clean and harmless, right?

Well . . . not exactly.

Spoiler: Our digital content has an emissions impact. So much
for that utopian ideal.

DATA HAS A CARBON FOOTPRINT

Around 2015, I was sitting in a client meeting in Germany, jet-lagged as hell. We were working on content strategy for yet another web redesign and overhaul, the third I'd been a part of. Someone in the interdepartmental meeting casually mentioned how all the old pages from two previous redesigns still existed, pages dating back a decade or more.

My jaw dropped. I was working with digital hoarders. I asked why they would keep all the old material. What were they saving it for?

"What if a customer bookmarked it?" the team worried. "We don't want them to be unable to find what they're looking for."

Never mind that the content was long outdated, sometimes even for products that had been discontinued. They wanted to keep the information and retain the links, regardless of the impact to usability.

It wasn't until I was wide awake in the hotel room at 2:00 a.m. that I started thinking about the cost of storing all that information in a data center. It must be astronomical! I went back into my emails and followed both staging and live links from 2009 and found everything from old sales decks to out-of-date videos. Gigabytes upon gigabytes of information, tucked away in storage like the crated-up Ark of the Covenant at the end of *Raiders of the Lost Ark*.

And that's when the obvious thought hit me: all the bits and bytes of digital content are data. Data is nothing more than energy. And energy—at least for the foreseeable future—has a carbon footprint. There is a direct connection between every web page, email campaign, or video meeting and carbon emissions. This realization stopped me in my tracks. I'd spent two decades creating vast amounts of digital content. This meant that I'd personally been responsible for a lot of greenhouse gas emissions. What was I doing? Could I still do what I do without damaging the planet? It was a question that I struggled with for a few years, but every time I brought up the topic with other content pros, I was met with blank stares or shrugs. "It can't be that bad," my content colleagues would say. "If it was, I would have heard about it."

UNCOVERING THE SUSTAINABLE CONTENT CONNECTION

I tried to step outside of the content universe and into the world of sustainability. Surely someone was talking about it there. After all, these are the people who think about climate impacts day in, day out. Right? Instead, I found that those sustainability experts were throwing data-intensive digital "solutions" at sustainability problems with the same reckless abandon as everyone else. Create an app, a podcast, a YouTube channel, an Instagram feed, or an NFT to build engagement! Machine learning, blockchain—these were the tools we needed to solve this crisis. Whether the problem was poverty or education, recycling or climate didn't matter. The solution was always digital. We were going to tech our way out of this mess!

I felt alone and isolated. Was it possible that no one else had noticed this? How is it that we're talking energy- and emissions-intensive options like blockchain, NFTs, and AI as a solution to climate issues? And who am I to say that everyone else is wrong? Despite my nerdy tendencies, I specialize in content, not science. What role does content play in the climate crisis, anyway?

But because I was absolutely, deeply certain that a connection existed, I decided to start by figuring out what I could do on a personal level. If I'm hired by my clients to create—if all of my professional metrics and paychecks are based on adding more and more—is there any way for me to mitigate that impact on future projects?

In April 2020, I stumbled across Gerry McGovern's book, *World Wide Waste*, thanks to the Quarantine Book Club Zoom calls run by Mule Design.[1] I already knew of McGovern's work on the Top Tasks framework, but I didn't know that he'd made the intellectual leap from connecting how the sheer volume of digital stuff affects the user experience to what all of it means in terms of sustainability.

"Digital is physical," he said in the April 2020 call, and I nearly fell off my chair.[2] Finally, someone else was voicing the same concerns. I had spent years shouting into the void within my client universe, and finally, someone was talking back.

A year later, Tom Greenwood published *Sustainable Web Design*.[3] Greenwood's book pointed out that roughly half of the weight of a web page is the image file. This showed me that this problem was equal parts content strategy (the planning for and governance of our content) and content design (serving the audience's needs through careful information structuring). This made the problem simultaneously more complex and more interesting.

I went down a rabbit hole of research to find out more. My family joked that I was mere days away from creating one of those whackadoodle wall boards, complete with red strings and pushpins to connect seemingly unrelated ideas in content, technology, energy, and sustainability. At the time, I thought that it all came back to the data center.

What I discovered was that I was thinking too small.

STARTING WITH STORAGE

For a long time, my tech background and its intense focus on data center operations gave me blinders about the data. If the client had a 4 MB web page, then I assumed that we were talking about the energy cost for storing that 4 MB of data and the repeated iterations thereof. Don't get me wrong: considering the number of websites out there, and the number of revisions we've made to any given web page over its lifespan, this is a lot of information.

But it wasn't just the current, live website that was sitting in the data center. As my client showed me, there was an entire ecosystem of dark data—information assets organizations collect, process, and store during regular business activities but generally fail to use for other purposes. This includes the backend tracking data and analytics that form the building blocks of business intelligence but more frequently sit unused and forgotten.

According to a 2021 survey report by Splunk, a California-based data software company, more than 60 percent of survey respondents said that half or more of their digital content is dark.[4] Lucidworks, a big data software company, estimates that more than 7.5 sextillion gigabytes of data are generated every day.[5] That's 7,500,000,000,000,000,000,000 GB—daily! If, as they suggest, 90 percent of it goes unused as dark data, that means that 6.75 sextillion gigabytes are archived and forgotten. "What good is all of this data if nobody is using more than a fraction of it?" asks the Splunk report.

Storing all these analytics and tracking data can have a greater risk than value for the organization, providing significant opportunity for harm embedded in tracked data. "Many companies choose to collect as much user data as they can, even if they don't have a stated use for that data," says Eva PenzeyMoog in *Design for Safety*.[6] That data—location, personal information, behavioral patterns, and more—gets stored away without any explicit purpose for it, leaving us vulnerable to security breaches and violations of the European Union's General Data Protection Regulation (GDPR).

As Splunk and Lucidworks showed, data centers are primarily data dumps, digital landfills that grow increasingly bloated every year. They're the place where we store and hoard the useless data that no one really wants but they're too afraid to throw away. That was the angle I'd been talking about with my clients: measuring the impact of storing that 4 MB for the rest of eternity "just in case." And as it's never just one page, one video, or one image-bloated slide deck, that data adds up.

And that was compelling! But something was nagging at the back of my mind, like the solution to a math problem that's just out of reach. The deeper I dove into the works of McGovern and Greenwood, the more I realized that I was looking at this all wrong. The real issue isn't in data storage: it's in data transfer.

MOVING DATA REQUIRES ENERGY

While archiving everything into the black hole of the data center is a problem, it's not about the energy required for the 4 MB for page version 1.0 (and another 12 MB for versions 1.1, 1.2, 1.3 . . .) to be parked in storage. Just like the junk stashed away in your basement, there's limited energy needed for it to just sit there. The real energy comes when you start moving it.

If a thousand people download that 4 MB web page, that's 4,000 MB (4 GB) of data transferred: 4 MB to me, 4 MB to you, and so on. When we're talking about corporate websites, we're looking at tens of thousands, possibly even millions of hits each year. The more successful the website, app, or podcast, the greater the climate impact. Gigabytes upon gigabytes of data are transferred. Kilowatts of energy are used.

Suddenly, we're looking at some serious numbers in terms of energy use and emissions. And with the International Panel on Climate Change (IPCC) reports forecasting dramatic and widespread impacts of climate change—impacts that we're already starting to feel—there's no time to lose in terms of reducing energy and emissions wherever we can.[7]

RELYING ON BEST PRACTICES

Easier said than done, right? Let's face it: change is hard. There are a number of psychological factors at play—the bias of our lived experience, our tendency to rely on gut instinct—but also our tendency to ignore risks and impacts that are simply too big for us to contemplate. While we are empathetic toward individuals, we do a terrible job of scaling that empathy toward broader populations. We tend to turn off our feelings in the wake of the unfathomable.

While there is certainly ample opportunity for bringing others on board to influence change, sustainable content doesn't require us to change others' belief systems. The changes that make content sustainable already fall within our sphere of influence as content professionals.

Fortunately, all our known content best practices, from plain language to governance, are sustainability friendly because they're about doing more with less. As it turns out, good content can play a role in changing the world. While we may not be able to single-handedly reverse climate change by altering our personal habits, we have a tremendous amount of opportunity for change at work.

In this book, I provide you with some foundational knowledge of sustainability—what it is and why it increasingly matters to business management and the planet as a whole. It's an emerging discipline with a language of its own, so I've provided a glossary and technical appendices at the end of the book. This will save you countless searches to decode acronyms and make sense of similarly worded terms that mean entirely different things.

Of course, we get into the reason that you're here. We examine the emissions cost of digital content, how we can measure that, and how it aligns with other content best practices. We've been conditioned to look at our personal lifestyle as the most important factor in slowing climate change. In reality, we have the most leverage at work.

One of our biggest challenges is that digital storage and distribution is financially cheap for the organization but ecologically costly for the world. We need to demonstrate that content, when created by skilled professionals and managed thoughtfully and carefully, is more than just a cost center. Sustainable content incorporates principles that improve usability, reduce costs, and improve customer satisfaction—affecting the bottom line.

Finally, we get into why sustainability conversations are so complex. What makes people resistant to discussing all of this? Why does it feel risky to discuss it? How can we use our content skills to gently influence and normalize these conversations? And why is it urgent that we do so immediately?

You are at the center of it all. By using your leverage at work, you can make a difference in the future of life on this planet.

Ready? Let's dig in.

CHAPTER 1

The Sustainability Opportunity

WALTER BURNS: We've been in worse jams
than this, haven't we, Hildy?

HILDY JOHNSON: Nope.

—His Girl Friday

WHEN I TALK ABOUT SUSTAINABILITY, most people think I'm talking about climate alone. There's no way to talk about climate without acknowledging that it's part of a vast, complex, and interconnected series of challenges.

We like to think of our world like a waffle. We want everything to fit into neat little squares with sharply defined boundaries: climate goes here, education goes there, and health is over on the other side. We structure our academic studies, our professional enterprises, and even our organizational departments as if they are unique, separate, and unrelated to everything around them. In reality, the world—and sustainability efforts—are more like a pancake: covered in a sticky syrup that disregards our neat little lines and gets everywhere.

A widely adopted definition states that sustainability is meeting the needs of the present without compromising future generations' ability to do the same. That's more complicated than it sounds.

"In a complex, interconnected world, it is simply impossible to do anything substantial or worthwhile that does not involve collaboration across multiple disciplines," writes Gerry McGovern in *Transform*.[1] We need to pool our resources and think outside the (waffle) box to achieve any sort of meaningful positive change in sustainability efforts.

THE NEED FOR INTERDISCIPLINARY THINKING

The idea of the lone genius hero is a screenwriter's dream. By the end of the third act, they have single-handedly tied up the loose plot threads, saved the world, and most likely found romance in the process.

I regret to inform you that sustainability will not work this way. This is complex stuff, and no one person has all the answers. We can't wait for a genius scientist with movie star hair or billionaire philanthropy to solve this problem. This is not something anyone can do alone.

"No one has the answers to the challenges facing citizens in this century, and everyone has the responsibility for trying and participating in finding them," says Liz Coleman, former president of Bennington College in Vermont in her TED Talk.[2] We require innovation, collaboration, and interdisciplinary thinking to improve life on Earth.

And, at least on the surface, people are receiving this message. It seems like every conference I've attended in the last decade has at least one session on bridging interdepartmental silos or fostering interdisciplinary thinking. But here's the problem: interdisciplinary thinking around sustainability is always approached as if it's a problem unique to corporations. In reality, the challenge goes deeper.

As Coleman notes, our educational system has trained us to think and teach in silos, preparing us to go deep into specialized areas without understanding interrelationships and codependences. We've been mistakenly taught that there are right and wrong answers for everything—fill in the bubble on the scoring sheet because the answer is a clear-cut A, B, C, or D, with no gray areas.

"Most adults' educational experiences do not prepare them well to deal with integrated, interdisciplinary problems that require agile responses and systems-thinking capabilities," write Susanne Moser and Lisa Dilling in *Creating a Climate for Change*.[3] Education has evolved to emphasize testable details in separate subject areas, rather than the connections among them.

We're no longer wiring our brains for complex systems thinking, just cause and effect. But systems are interconnected. "Systems happen all at once," writes Donella H. Meadows in *Thinking in Systems*. "They are connected not just in one direction, but in many directions simultaneously."[4]

We need to look at how the different puzzle pieces fit together. Interconnectedness was the rationale behind the creation of the

Sustainable Development Goals (SDGs) by the United Nations.[5] Established in 2015, the 17 goals were designed to set forth a "blueprint for peace and prosperity," acknowledging that there are multiple building blocks of an equitable, sustainable world that we'd all want to live in. (See Appendix A for a list of all SDGs.)

The SDGs fall into a few broad categories:

- The future of work and employability: jobs and the education needed for them

- Social protections: health, equality, and justice

- Quality of life: eliminating hunger, poverty, and inequality

- Circular economy: the consumption and reuse of resources

- Environment: climate action, life on land, and life below water

Each of the SDGs is part of a complex, adaptive system and can't be solved in isolation. We can't resolve overfishing without understanding the impacts of poverty and lack of education in the coastal communities that rely on fishing income. We can't understand good health without understanding how social inequality contributes to vastly different healthcare access and health outcomes. Everything is connected.

For many people, an awareness of the scope and scale of sustainability is relatively new. The pandemic era revealed just how brittle and intertwined our world can be. Concerns about health, poverty, climate, social justice, food supply, and education have all been pushed to the forefront of our minds since 2020. We saw that, much like in the game of Jenga, if you destabilize one area, everything else can come tumbling down.

Most of us have been trying to push ahead like everything is normal, the living embodiment of the "This is fine" meme, sitting with our cup of coffee while everything around us is in flames. But it also led to a lot of people throwing their hands in the air and saying, "I'm just one person. What can I do to fix all of this?"

Even those of us who have been in this for a long time are trying to answer that question. But I know that the solutions will not come in isolation.

SUSTAINABILITY MOVES
TO THE FOREGROUND

For most of my lifetime, climate change has been background noise. Environmentalists were perceived to be a small, fringe group of protesters outside nuclear power plants or preventing logging in old-growth forests. While some individuals in my circle may have had their concerns about the environment (or any of the themes within the SDGs), it wasn't something that was integrated into everyday discussions.

There was no mention of its connection to investing by any-one I talked to while doing long-term temp work at a brokerage in the mid-1990s. Working at a jewelry magazine in the late 1990s brought awareness of the impacts of gem and metals mining on the local community, but not the bigger picture of how that affected the broader environment or economic and political instability in the region. Tech companies talked about data center issues in terms of direct financial costs of electricity to operate and cool servers, not environmental impacts. It was never a primary talking point at healthcare organizations—at least, not at my individual contributor level.

That started to change for my clients a year or two before the COVID-19 pandemic. Suddenly, all my clients were talking about reducing their use of water and energy, recycling materials, and minimizing single-use plastics. Walmart and UPS ordered electric semitrucks in 2018.[6] In 2019, Levi's promoted their Water<Less process that used 96 percent less water in garment manufacturing.[7] And according to *Forbes*, corporate solar panel installation soared in the second half of the 2010s.[8] But still the context was primarily financially influenced in the form of reducing costs for themselves or their customers, rather than for decarbonization initiatives.

"Top companies are increasingly investing in clean, reliable solar energy because it makes economic sense," noted Abigail Hooper, president and CEO of the Solar Energy Industries Association (SEIA) in the *Forbes* article. This isn't exclusively environmental altruism.

A few years later, sustainability seems to be everywhere at the consumer level. From plastic bag bans to Amazon electric delivery vans to increasing awareness of the environmental and social impact of fast fashion, multiple factors have converged to bring the topic of sustainability to the forefront. It's no longer buried in SEC filings or a deep subpage on the "About Us" section of the website. It's a key part of consumer marketing. For example,

Nordstrom has been highlighting its sustainably and ethically produced products in emails as well as in its product descriptions.

In a survey conducted by BCG in 2020, people reported being more aware of human activity and its connection to climate than they were in prepandemic times.[9] This has created an interesting feedback loop: increased awareness leads to heightened expectations, heightened expectations drive corporate initiatives, and corporate initiatives further increase awareness.

Urgency and Hope

Even though we're moving forward with sustainability initiatives, awareness, and messaging, we still have a long way to go to make a measurable impact in mitigating atmospheric emissions. The 10 warmest years in recorded history have occurred since 2010, and the 2020s are on pace to be the hottest decade yet.[10] In sustainability circles, the dark humor goes something like this: "This wasn't the hottest summer of your life. It was the coolest summer of the rest of your life." Cue weak laughter.

Our atmospheric carbon dioxide levels have been consistently increasing. The National Oceanic and Atmospheric Administration (NOAA) has been monitoring the atmosphere at the Mauna Loa Observatory in Hawaii since the late 1950s, the longest such example of continuous monitoring (Figure 1.1). While seasonal fluctuations do occur (seen in the zigzagging line), the steeply upward trend of increased emissions continues unabated.

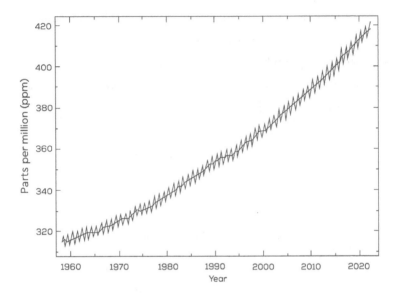

Figure 1.1. Atmospheric CO$_2$ at Mauna Loa Observatory. Atmospheric emissions continue to increase steeply with each passing year. (Source: National Oceanic and Atmospheric Administration, "Monthly Average Mauna Loa CO$_2$," April 5, 2024, https://gml.noaa.gov/ccgg/trends/.)

There's a lag time between emissions and their effects. The changes that we're seeing today are a result of emissions from roughly a decade ago. Even if the entire planet were to abandon fossil fuels and switch to zero-emission renewable energy sources tomorrow, it will be another decade before the tide turns and we start to see improvements. This is why we need to take swift and decisive action today. (For more information about fossil fuels and renewable energy, see Appendix B.)

Anthropogenic (human-influenced) climate change is expected to have significant impacts on the health and well-being of all humans, resulting in more intense heatwaves, higher risks of flooding and damaging storms, and a changing pattern of emerging infectious diseases.

This sounds dark and dismal, but there is some hope. Look at the potential impacts of the Inflation Reduction Act of 2022, which, despite its confusing name, was the biggest single climate legislation that the world has ever seen.[11] It includes billions of investment dollars set aside for decarbonization, energy security, rural resilience, conservation, energy cost reductions, and addressing disproportionate climate and health impacts. This program will address a variety of the SDGs discussed previously, including reducing poverty in industrial or rural communities, increasing professional and technical education, and improving health and well-being. It ensures a just transition that retrains individuals and secures workers' livelihoods during the period of transformation.

These are significant steps forward that will have ripple effects beyond U.S. borders because nothing happens in isolation. But it's also set the bar for other regions and nations to propose legislation, such as the Green Deal Industrial Plan that was announced by the European Union in early 2023.[12]

The COVID-19 Pandemic Changed Our Perspective

For many people, prior to the pandemic shutdowns of 2020, it was easy to sweep sustainability issues under the rug. How much did people of privilege really experience the impacts of climate change, of public health concerns, or of social justice issues? (Everyone reading this book is likely privileged in the global sense:

we are literate and probably earn more than $18,000 USD per year.) We spoke earlier about the BCG report in which 70 percent of survey participants said that they were more aware of the impacts now than they were prepandemic. The World Economic Forum refers to it as an "eco-wakening," with a rise in searches for sustainable goods.[13]

But the 2020s have revealed that climate impacts are closer than we thought. We saw climate change become real in the apocalypse-orange skies of California and the horrible wildfires in Australia and Canada. We've witnessed hurricanes so numerous that we ran out of names for them. We saw the uneven impacts of comorbidities affecting patient outcomes in the pandemic and the consequences of watching an overburdened healthcare system struggle to keep up. Low-income and special needs students struggled with remote learning, deficits that linger three years in.

Different countries had different access to vaccines, with some individuals refusing shots while others were dying while waiting for access. High-profile amateur videos highlighted police brutality, and mainstream coverage began acknowledging what people of color had known all along: that people are treated differently based on the color of their skin. It became clear that the world was changing rapidly and that not all populations were experiencing that change at the same pace or in the same way.

We exposed a lot of raw nerves all at once. And being stuck at home, we all had a lot of time to be immersed in an onslaught of information about it. This only reinforced the feeling of powerlessness, the "I'm just one person" problem. What can we do?

We're already seeing these effects play out on the global stage.

According to the Intergovernmental Panel on Climate Change (IPCC), human-induced changes to the climate system are already widespread.[14] However, entrenched, systemic inequalities make the situation worse. The impacts will be unevenly felt, with more dramatic consequences experienced by women,[15] those experiencing poverty,[16] and Black, Indigenous, and people of color (BIPOC).[17] For example, after the 2004 Indian Ocean earthquake and tsunami, nearly three-quarters of the deaths were female. And globally, people of color are more likely to experience the first and worst effects of worsening heat and natural disasters. Climate is a threat multiplier, accelerating existing instabilities and worsening health, inequality, and hunger on a global scale.

My Complicated History with Sustainability

If you're like me, you've probably been fed conflicting information about your role in all of this, which varies wildly between gatekeepers telling you "You're not doing enough" to others arguing that you're just going to get in the way of the grown-ups who are solving this problem.

Let's take a trip back in time. I grew up three blocks from a federal Superfund site near Philadelphia, Pennsylvania, and spent my summers swimming in the community pool next door. Superfund is a federal government program to identify and clean up the most contaminated sites in the country. You are no doubt envisioning me as someone who bears more than a passing resemblance to the three-eyed fish from *The Simpsons* at this point, and I don't blame you.

We were a community of limited means and Title 1 schools with a high percentage of households living in poverty, the kind of place that was a natural dumping ground for businesses that knew that we didn't have the resources to push back. My mother was a regular fixture at planning commission meetings. She was, no doubt, a recurring thorn in the side of the council members who just wanted the much-needed tax revenue, regardless of the long-term consequences.

It seems natural, then, that I would have grown up with an interest in sustainability and environmental justice. I was one of the founding members of my high school's environmental club in the late 1980s. Our goal was to bring a fledgling recycling program to the school (how quaint!) and eliminate ozone-depleting aerosols from the janitors' closets. We thought this was some pioneering stuff at the time. (Let's just take a moment to realize that within my lifetime, recycling was considered a newfangled idea that we needed to advocate for, rather than a standard fixture in our lives.)

I wanted more information about how we could build and grow our club to extend its impact. So I wrote a letter to an organization in Berkeley, California (not affiliated with the university), that I read about in *Sassy* magazine. I asked them: What could a small group of motivated teens do to make a difference in the world?

A few weeks later, I received what I will forever think of as "The Letter of Shame." What I expected was for the organization to say, "Hey, great start, kids, here's where some similar groups have gone next." What I got was a dismissive, holier-than-thou screed about how this was the absolute *least* we could do. It did everything short

22

of outright calling us losers for starting with recycling and ozone because we weren't doing a dozen other things. It literally said that our efforts were "embarrassing" and that if we weren't willing to be part of the solution, then we were part of the problem. I was so mortified and humiliated that I crumpled the letter, threw it in the recycling bin, and didn't speak of it again for nearly 30 years. My cheeks still burn when I think of it.

Naturally, I decided that I needed to do more, but I got conflicting messages. I remember discussing college planning with the club advisor. I had been an intensely math- and science-focused child, and I contemplated studying something in the context of environmental science. "You don't want to do that," he said. "They'll have all of this solved in the next decade, and then what will you do with that degree?"

Misleading career counseling aside, all this feedback led to a pervasive sense of exclusion. On one hand, I wasn't doing enough, so I shouldn't even try. On the other hand, other people were handling it, and I should just step aside and not even try. Part of me has always carried the burden of being stuck somewhere in between. I didn't feel like there was a place for me—someone who grew up to be a self-employed content professional—to do something.

There's a Place for You

Don't get me wrong: there is always a push and pull between "other people will solve this" and the gatekeepers who are forever angry that you're not doing enough. This book occupies a middle ground, a safe space for the majority of the population that's climate concerned but not necessarily climate vocal. And yes, studies show that you are in the majority, even if it doesn't feel that way.[18]

If you take nothing else from this book, remember that there is a place for you in all of this. We've reached an all-hands-on-deck moment. While this book talks about sustainable content, the most important takeaway is that everyone everywhere has a role in making our world better. There is no right or wrong way to do it. There is, however, quite a bit of urgency.

None of us are immune to the long-term impacts of climate change. The 2022 IPCC Summary for Policymakers notes that "near-term actions that limit global warming to close to 1.5°C would substantially reduce projected losses and damages related to climate change in human systems and ecosystems."[19] We will all feel the effects of storms, heat, food scarcity, supply chain disruptions, and health implications within the coming decades.

While the consequences of inaction are far reaching and scary, we have both the opportunity to make a difference and the ethical obligation to act wherever we can. With our shared resources and knowledge, we can begin to address these challenges. We have a personal and professional opportunity to make changes that truly have an impact on the world. You can use your leverage at work to have an impact. The time to act is now.

OUR RESPONSIBILITY

I was living in California on September 9, 2020. I fumbled to turn off my alarm in the dark. The birds weren't chirping, and what little light peeked through the curtains was entirely the wrong color. During the ever-lengthening drought-fueled wildfire season, it wasn't uncommon for us to wake to smoke-dulled skies and weak morning light. But this was different. And it was terrifying.

It was what Californians would later think of as "Orange Day," the day that the skies turned the color of fire, the sun was a barely visible disc in the sky at noon, and ash fell to the ground like snow flurries. We'd crossed a tipping point. Even someplace as insular and economically protected as Silicon Valley was still vulnerable.

For many people, especially Californians in the technology sector, it was a wake-up call. Those who believed that climate change was a slow-moving disaster in far-off lands or the distant future were starting to consider the possibility that maybe, just maybe, the effects were more local and immediate. Maybe we weren't going to be able to sweep this climate stuff under the rug and pretend it's not going to affect us.

Maybe our choices matter.

But what can one person do? It's easy to fall victim to a mental paralysis about all of this, a psychic numbing that we discuss in more detail in Chapter 7. Studies have shown that impassivity is a result of the suppression of emotion in the face of a distressing situation: this problem is too big, and because I'm overwhelmed, I'll just do nothing.[20]

That's why we're here today, talking about this in measurable, actionable ways. And one of the most actionable ways is by influencing systems larger than ourselves. The biggest lever for change is at the organizational level.

We Have the Most Leverage at Work

For decades, we've heard about our climate or carbon footprint: the impact that our lives and choices have on the Earth's climate. Why do we know about carbon footprints? While it was a term developed by scientists, it became famous after a BP marketing campaign that began about 20 years ago and is still used today. BP—yes, the corporation formerly known as British Petroleum—wanted to shift the emphasis to personal responsibility to draw attention away from the fact that BP is the fifth largest polluter in human history.

It was a remarkably effective campaign, and it shifted the conversation away from corporations, placing the weight entirely on the shoulders of the individual. It allowed us to get bogged down by shaming each other for using plastic straws or driving older, less efficient cars. It was a distraction, turning our attention from the real problem: them.

In truth, most carbon emissions have come from a handful of corporations. According to the 2017 "Carbon Majors Report" published by the Carbon Disclosure Project (CDP), the not-for-profit organization that runs the global disclosure system, 100 companies are responsible for more than half of all greenhouse gas emissions since the start of the Industrial Revolution 250 years ago. These organizations—including BP, as mentioned earlier—are responsible for 71 percent of all emissions since 1998.[21]

As the International Energy Agency noted in its report "Net Zero by 2050," no individual lifestyle changes have as much impact as those we make at work.[22] Yes, of course, it's important to vote and make personal changes; we need all the help we can get to meet our goals. But even the most aggressively antienvironmental individual behaviors—short trips on private jets or big pickup trucks adapted to roll coal—don't add up to a fraction of what's happening at the corporate level.

Individual Change Doesn't Change Much

Thanks in part to BP, even sustainability conferences focus on four big changes that can be made at the personal level: get solar, drive an EV, change your diet, and avoid flying. But this approach has a very White, suburban, U.S. focus. But even in the United States, there are large swaths of the population for whom these aren't doable. However, as we've been conditioned to think in terms of personal change, we'll use the big four personal changes to context-set the scale of individual impacts versus what we can achieve in the workplace.

- *Not everyone has access to or the funds for solar:* Household solar has the most impact on an individual's carbon footprint. In sunny Phoenix, my solar array has avoided more than 21.9 tons (19.9 metric tons) of greenhouse gas emissions. However, this option isn't open to the 36 percent of Americans who rent their homes or apartments and can be limited in the 53 percent of owner-occupied households governed by homeowners association (HOA) restrictions.[23] It's also not cheap and requires a strong credit score to qualify.

- *Electric vehicles require accessible infrastructure:* Replacing an internal combustion vehicle with an electric vehicle (EV) can eliminate 4.9 tons (4.45 metric tons) of emissions per year.[24] But that assumes a single-family home with a garage equipped for overnight charging. Of course, we could reduce even more emissions with public transit or cycling, but with limited public transportation and safe cycling options in most of the United States, the ability to switch modes is unavailable for most people. The large-scale infrastructure changes required to support more environmentally friendly modes of transportation aren't going to happen overnight.

- *Your diet matters less than you think:* We know that meat and dairy have significant climate impacts. We can choose to go vegan as a way to mitigate our impacts. This turns out to have a smaller impact on our climate footprints than expected. Most early studies assumed that vegans would eat plant-based, locally grown diets. In practice, they eat meat substitutes, nut milks, tofu, and even Oreos. All those foods are highly processed and contribute to your carbon footprint.

- *Eliminating travel:* What if we never fly again? Eliminating air travel saves more greenhouse gas emissions than changes in diet do. And, of course, if you're in a position to have a private jet (as all content professionals are, obviously), just a one-hour flight emits the equivalent of one-fourth of the annual carbon footprint of the average European citizen.[25]

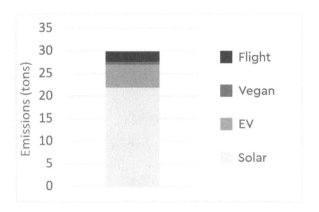

Figure 1.2. The four largest personal changes that we can make add up to avoiding nearly 30 tons of carbon dioxide emissions each year.

Putting all this individual change together—solar, EVs, dietary habits, and restricted commercial air travel—can help you avoid up to nearly 30 tons (27.1 metric tons) of annual greenhouse gas emissions, equivalent to removing 5.8 gasoline-fueled cars from the road each year (Figure 1.2).

Of course, everything we do adds up, no matter how small. However, we need to be realistic about the scope of change that BP has placed on our individual shoulders. Even if every human implements personal behavioral changes where we can, it still only reduces greenhouse gas emissions by about 4 percent by 2050.[26] We need to think bigger. That's why we need to use our leverage in the workplace.

THE CAPITALIST CASE FOR CARBON MITIGATION

Even the most die-hard capitalist is starting to realize that we have finite resources to draw on, from clean water to rare earth minerals, and the pandemic highlighted the limitations to human capital. As a result, the systems are now incentivizing sustainability to build resilience into operational planning and deliver a long-term return on investments.

Should ROI be our goal? Of course not. But for once, traditional economic incentives are starting to align with what we need to accomplish from a sustainability perspective. To me, it doesn't matter if BigCo installs solar arrays to gain tax breaks or avoid disruptions from rolling blackouts. The end result is the same: reduced use of fossil fuels and fewer emissions. Companies like Apple and Chipotle are tying executive compensation to sustainability metrics, and we know that nothing motivates management quite like compensation. We're finally pulling the cart in the same direction.

But how do you fit into this? You're probably reluctant to talk about all of this sustainability stuff at work. Isn't that professionally risky? After all, the science is still up for debate, and the public is pretty evenly split about this whole climate thing, right? You don't want to take the risk of talking about it at work, do you?

Funny thing about that. We think that not everyone is on board with the science because media coverage has tricked us into believing there's a 50-50 split in the scientific consensus about climate change. You know what I mean: scientists release a study, so to get a "balanced" perspective on the peer-reviewed paper, the news also interviews a politician, an old guy in a diner, and a podcaster to get their opinions. Usually all male, usually all White.

Whether or not the politician, diner guy, and podcaster agree, we're at nearly 100 percent consensus on anthropogenic climate change within the scientific community. I discuss this and the public perception of it more in Chapter 7.

IPCC data shows that human-induced warming has already reached approximately 1.1°C above preindustrial levels and is projected to increase by 0.2°C per decade going forward.[27] This—to put it bluntly—is not good. However, decades of shouting about the impacts haven't really moved the needle, so let's get down to the essence of what might matter in our capitalist system: rising temperatures are incredibly bad for business.

"The 2020s will be the most disruptive decade in history," according to James Arbib and Tony Seba of the not-for-profit think tank RethinkX. "COVID-19 has simply pulled the curtain on the fragility of current models of production and governance. It is just one of a series of predictable shocks that threaten to devastate our civilization if, collectively, we do not make the right choices."[28]

How devastating? We're looking at significant physical risk. At 2°C over preindustrial levels, Moody's Analytics says that "climate change could inflict $69 trillion in damage on the global economy by 2100."[29] This feels like a lowball estimate to me considering that in 2021 alone, there were more than 20 separate billion-dollar climate disasters totaling $145 billion. In the United States alone, we've spent more than $2.6 trillion on climate disasters in the past four decades.[30] Keep in mind that at the current rate of 0.2°C per decade, we'll hit the 2.0°C mark soon and be well beyond it by 2100.

The Moody's Analytics report notes that human health is sensitive to shifts in weather patterns and other aspects of climate change, disproportionately affecting women and BIPOC communities. It also affects our frontline workers in retail, food service, construction, transport, and many other industries that are crucial to keeping the economy going. It will hit them first, but the ripple effects will eventually have an impact on those of us in climate-controlled offices.

The Economy Requires a Healthy Workforce

Rising temperatures will universally hurt all worker health and productivity. Both acute illnesses (like COVID-19 or monkeypox) and chronic illnesses (asthma, diabetes, long COVID, or Lyme disease) will become more prevalent, reducing the available labor force. We're already seeing a tightening of the workforce. As of April 2023, the United States alone has lost more than 273,000 individuals between the working ages of 18 and 64 to COVID-related deaths (not including excess mortality from other conditions that went untreated during the pandemic because of strain on the healthcare system).[31] A 2022 study showed that 1.6 million Americans had symptoms of long COVID that limited their ability to work. They estimate that long COVID could be accounting for 15 percent of the labor shortage.[32]

In 2021, the Pew Research Center noted that the decrease in labor force participation understates the share of Americans who are out of work. In 2022, Stanford researchers estimated that the U.S. labor force has been reduced by half a million because of COVID-19-related illness.[33] As the pandemic was a worldwide phenomenon, it's reasonable to assume that similar limitations are present in other nations' employment data as well.[34] Businesses are starting to understand that human capital is an increasingly limited resource.

Beyond impacts on individual workers, how is this happening, and what will it look like?

- The physical costs of climate change will compound slowly over time in a snowball effect.[35]

- Forecasts predict that the worst of the effects, such as natural disasters, will not be felt until 2030 and beyond, and will increasingly disrupt and damage critical infrastructure and property.[36]

- Climate change carries vast geopolitical risk, as noted by the U.S. Department of Defense.[37]

- Impacts will be unevenly felt in different geographical regions; the impact of rising sea levels and increased hurricanes on coastal Tampa may be different than the whole of Florida, which will be different from the broader United States.[38]

"The real question is not simply 'How much will it cost us to avoid (or reduce) climate change?'" says John Atcheson of the U.S. Department of Energy. "Rather, it is 'How much will it cost us if we don't?'"[39]

We're Running Out of Resources

We know that our impact on our natural environment exceeds our capacity. In 2022, Earth Overshoot Day—the day by which

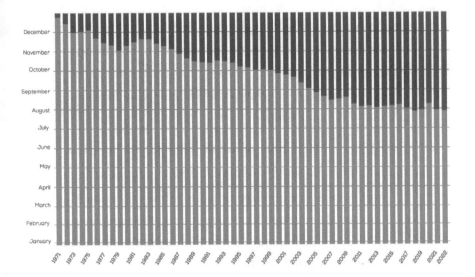

Figure 1.3. Earth Overshoot Day, 1971–2022. In the last five decades, we have depleted the planet's natural resources at an accelerating rate. (Source: Earth Overshoot Day, "Earth Overshoot Day, 1971–2022" accessed April 9, 2023, https://www.overshootday.org/.)

we used all the resources that the planet can regenerate in a year—fell on July 28 (Figure 1.3). That means that for 43 percent of the year, we were exceeding the planet's ability to sustain us.

This has repercussions not just for now but for generations to come. Our modern post–Industrial Revolution economy is built on extraction and exploitation, not simply of natural resources (sometimes referred to by the very capitalist term of "natural capital") but of human capital as well. "Economics is a system for optimizing resources, and if it were trying to calculate ways to optimize a sustainable civilization in balance with the biosphere, it could be a helpful tool," says author Kim Stanley Robinson in an article for the *New Yorker* in May 2020.[40] "When it's used to optimize profit, however, it encourages us to live within a system of destructive falsehoods. We need a new political economy by which to make our calculations."

This is obviously an ethical issue, but it's also a coldhearted numbers issue: if you run out of resources to extract and exploit, then you've lost the foundation for your profit engine. "As with previous civilizations, the extraction system of production continues to work in favor of a core demographic, while exploiting other groups," say Arbib and Seba.[41] Most of the world is structured around the idea that economic growth equals prosperity. It's a mindset that won't change overnight. Therefore, continued economic growth needs to be built on different approaches.

"Faced with mathematical laws and biophysical limits, future economies will not be able to prop themselves up by way of ever-increasing consumption and throughput," explains political theorist Dr. Leslie Paul Thiele in his book *Sustainability*. "[We] have hit the 'end of growth' and now must adapt to a 'new economic reality.'"[42]

And that reality means that we must change the way we do business because only sustainable businesses will be resilient enough to withstand this transition. (For insights into the history of regulation and its impact on climate change, see Appendix C.)

YOUR LEVERAGE IS YOUR POWER

If most emissions are driven by corporations—not individuals—then it makes sense that we have the most leverage for change at work. Our impacts there can substantially exceed even our most drastic personal changes. And now that capitalism is starting to connect externalities with long-term business resilience, there are incentives for organizations to look for more sustainable ways of doing business.

As we see in the next chapter, our digital communications have a direct energy and emissions impact. The largest scale examples of digital content all come at the organizational level. Therefore, we have an obligation to leverage our influence where we can, and we have the greatest opportunity for influence at work.

CHAPTER 2

Sustainable Content Is Good Content

Let me explain. No, there is too much. Let me sum up.

—INIGO MONTOYA, *The Princess Bride*

I HAVE AN OFFICE COVERED with thousands of important words, phrases, and quotes documented on to-do lists, jotted on index cards, or meticulously handwritten in notebooks or journals. This doesn't mean that this content is useful to anyone but me (and even that is debatable). My office is the physical embodiment of a terrible user experience.

Contrary to what we were taught in school, effective communication isn't about meeting word counts. Good content is about quality, not quantity. So, what makes good content *good*? Quality content needs to be:

- *Accessible:* built for effective use by everyone at all levels of ability and comprehension

- *Usable:* easy for an audience to achieve the desired outcome

- *Sustainable:* adding value today without compromising the needs of future generations

You're probably already looking out for those first two, and now you may be wondering how to incorporate one more metric into your arsenal. How does this fit in? The good news is that sustainable content generally takes a "less is more" approach to communication, reducing both cognitive load and energy demands. It aligns with existing best practices. But none of that happens without a solid plan.

Content strategy requires that we approach our content development with a plan. This sounds obvious, but I've worked with more than a few clients where the strategy is "willy-nilly creation based on the changing whims of management." That plan can be reduced to three primary questions:

- Who are we creating for? Why are they here, and what do they need to accomplish?

- What do they need? How can we make it easy for them to achieve their goals?

- Are we adding value? Does this thing—a web page, video, email, podcast—offer a true audience benefit, or is it just noise and emissions?

The value element is where sustainable content sits. How do we balance the trade-offs between communication and environmental impact? Let's look at how we can approach our content wisely and sustainably.

PUTTING THE AUDIENCE FIRST

"Writing begins where all design and engineering starts: identifying the purposes, opportunities, and constraints for the experience," says Torrey Podmajersky in her book *Strategic Writing for UX*. "The writer needs to identify the goals of the person who will use the experience as well as the goals of the organization making the experience."[1]

Every project needs to start from the outside and work inward, although many organizations desperately want to work the other way around. I can clearly remember a scenario when I worked in-house at a major tech company in the early 2000s. The product manager came to me with a list of new features that he wanted to communicate for the Widget 2.0 launch. These were, at best, incremental changes that were largely irrelevant to the user, yet things had changed just enough to require an entirely new set of materials, from web pages to documentation. As I scrolled down the list, my eye caught on the most comical: "CTA button is now blue."

"These are features," I said. "What are the benefits to our customers?" He stared blankly and reiterated that these were talking points for launch. I pointed to the item about the button. "How does this solve a problem or differentiate us from the competition?"

A look of relief crossed his face. "Oh, none of our competitors have a blue button."

Of course. How could I be so oblivious? Six months later, after leaving the company, I saw that they not only had created all new digital content but also hadn't deleted the old. Customers were complaining in forums that they couldn't find the information they needed because they couldn't differentiate between old and new. The changes led to increased calls to the help desk: more time, more frustration, more downloads of digital resources, more energy used, and more cost for the company. Management never likes to see that kind of hit to the bottom line.

Google's design guide says it simply: "Focus on the user and all else will follow."[2] In the case of the blue button, we clearly weren't doing that. But what does that mean, practically speaking? It means that if we're doing our jobs correctly, we remove friction to help the audience learn or do things.

"Our words aren't there to be read, savored and appreciated, but to pass unremembered while they help to get somebody to the thing they want," says Podmajersky.[3] And the clearer it is, the easier it is to use.

"Clear communication in plain language starts with a clear understanding of the audience and respect for the audience's needs for information," says Russell Willerton in *Plain Language and Ethical Action*. "It entails not merely involving the audience but demonstrating deep, ongoing concern for the audience's needs for information."[4] Do all users want the same thing? Yes and no. While different personas may have different goals, we all have the same fundamental needs for our content. The easier we make it to find what they're looking for, the less energy they have to expend to find it—literally and mentally.

STRATEGY ACROSS CHANNELS

We have a variety of tools at our disposal that enable us to reach our audience in the most effective ways possible. Text, graphics, and structure all play a role in effectively communicating our message. Pictures, diagrams, charts, videos, calendars, and maps can all tell a story that helps with clear and effective communication. However, we need to be conscious of the fact that there is no one-size-fits-all tool that serves all customer needs. A video may be the most effective tool for building customer engagement with a product demo. Conversely, it may be the least effective form of engagement if your glossy vanity project has no substance.

If strategic communication is an organization's purposeful use of communication to fulfill its mission, then that's central to the role of every professional communicator. We are all purposeful influencers. "You cannot deliver a complete product or service without good information about it," say content strategists Rahel Anne Bailie and Noz Urbina. "Your content is not only your intellectual property, it is the ambassador of your brand."[5]

Customer satisfaction demands quality content. In fact, the most effective channels used for customer acquisition or retention are content driven:

- Email
- Social media
- Content marketing
- Referral marketing
- SEO

- Display/mobile advertising

- Video

- Documentation

Notice that these are all largely digital content resources. If our digital content has an emissions cost, it matters that our organization's message is presented effectively and strategically. "Good strategic communication is like Esperanto," write Chip and Dan Heath in their book *Made to Stick*. "It facilitates communication among people who have different native languages and carves out turf that people can share."[6]

Many channels fall into the increasingly blurry area between a variety of communications departments. The internal silos of technical communication, marketing communication, public relations, investor relations, internal communications, and product marketing are irrelevant to the audience. As each group operates independently, they re-create the wheel with overlapping forms of digital content creation.

"We need to pivot and start infusing new words, language, and concepts into the way we see ourselves contributing to the digital and project economy," writes Dr. Liz Herman in her 2020 *Technical Communicator* journal article, "Identity Disruption and the Technical Communicator."[7] She notes that as digital content creators, we have always been at the forefront of audience-centric content development.

And we're in luck that content is increasingly being seen as an asset, according to the World Economic Forum's July 2020 briefing paper, "A New Paradigm for Business of Data."[8] The report says that by 2025, 49 percent of the world's data will be in public cloud environments; nearly 30 percent will be in real time, allowing for faster and contextualized decision-making. What drives that decision-making? The content that we create. And to create that content effectively, we need to focus on how it is designed.

GOOD CONTENT DESIGN

"I take care to distinguish 'Does it look easy to read?' from 'Is it actually easy to read?' as criteria, because these are two separate, but equally important factors in whether or not your content is successful," says David Dylan Thomas in *Design for Cognitive Bias*. "A help article may use the plainest language in the world, but if it looks like it's going to be hard to read, users will never know how approachable it is because they will never read it."[9]

In *Letting Go of the Words*, Ginny Redish gave six guidelines for focusing on your essential messaging.[10] I want to focus on three of them: cutting content, starting with the key point, and breaking down walls of words.

Cut, Cut, Cut

Give people only the useful information they need. More is not always better. Cutting is crucial. When we cut content down, we reduce the cognitive load. As seen in everything from hospital discharge paperwork to product documentation, readers can be inundated with information but can't find what's needed.

Work with your UX research and support teams to identify

that sweet spot. "Getting UX research into the hands of product team members empowers them to create with the user in mind, which contributes to the product's usability and ultimate success," says UX researcher Gini Martinez in a 2022 article for *Intercom* magazine.[11] Then follow up with support to see how the updates have changed the user experience. If your changes are leading to increased help desk calls, you still aren't providing what's needed. Iterate the content in collaboration with these two teams to deliver exactly what customers are looking for.

Start with the Key Point

Write in an inverted pyramid style (see the left side of Figure 2.1). Get to the point. The inverted pyramid style encourages us to put the most important information first. Depending on the situation, this is where we tell *who* we are, *what* we do, *where* we are, *when* something is happening, *why* it matters, or *how* to accomplish a task. Ideally, someone reading our page, app, email, social media post, or video will be able to know if this is the right page for their needs without ever having to scroll.

We know from eye-tracking studies that people focus the most on the top of the page and then proceed down in an F pattern.[12] This triangle is not all that different from the inverted pyramid. We search for the most important information at the top of the page and then work our way down (see the right side of Figure 2.1). If we don't find what we're looking for, we'll go to another page: another few megabytes downloaded, a little more energy used, more greenhouse gas emissions added to

Figure 2.1. The inverted pyramid structure of information delivery, familiar to journalists everywhere (left), and the F pattern of web reading, identified by eye-tracking studies (right). Our eyes look for important information at the top of the page and then down along the left side.

the atmosphere. Interestingly, as noted by Redish, blind readers follow a similar set of reading behaviors online. Using screen readers, they listen to only a few words before deciding to jump to the next heading or paragraph.[13] Following these best practices is also a win for accessibility.

Break Down Walls of Words

The design and presentation of the content can be just as important as the words themselves. Let's break down those walls of words. There are more than 170,000 words in the English language, and sometimes it feels like all of them are in that one solid block of text. Table 2.1 shows the same Lorem Ipsum text presented in two formats. Which looks more approachable for the reader? Which is skimmable? Which is more likely to result in a reader abandoning this page and downloading another? Sometimes what we interpret as user engagement—visiting multiple pages—is actually a sign of confusion. If they don't find the answer they need here, they'll

Table 2.1. Text shown in two different formats

Lorem ipsum dolor sit amet, consectetur adipiscing elit, sed do eiusmod tempor incididunt ut labore et dolore magna aliqua. Ut enim ad minim veniam, quis nostrud exercitation ullamco laboris nisi ut aliquip ex ea commodo consequat. Duis aute irure dolor in reprehenderit in voluptate velit esse cillum dolore eu fugiat nulla pariatur. Excepteur sint occaecat cupidatat nonofficial, sunt in culpa qui-official deserunt mollit anim id est laborum.	Lorem ipsum dolor sit amet. Consectetur adipiscing elit. • Sed do eiusmod tempor incididunt ut labore et dolore magna aliqua • Ut enim ad minim veniam • Quis nostrud exercitation ullamco laboris • Nisi ut aliquip ex ea commodo consequat • Duis aute irure dolor in reprehenderit in voluptate velit. Esse cillum dolore eu fugiat nulla pariatur. Excepteur sint occaecat cupidatat nonofficial, sunt in culpa qui-official deserunt mollit anim id est laborum.

search elsewhere. More pages. More energy. More emissions. In this example, the text on the right is more approachable and readable.

CONTENT SHOULD ADD VALUE

There's an art to the way words and imagery are combined to communicate effectively. And while a good picture may be worth a thousand words, the use of generic stock art can detract from our message. Modern web design—the splash image or video taking up the bulk of the space above the fold—not only is unsustainable and data intensive but also violates the logic of the inverted pyramid. Think about your bank's website, for example. In most cases, there's a large image taking up most of the real estate on the page: a woman using a mobile phone, two people looking at blueprints, a smiling family at a picnic table. Our eyes are drawn to faces, which brings our attention away from the F pattern where the actual information lives, like the login or account information. Large images also increase the weight of a web page, requiring more energy to transfer and generating more emissions.

In these examples, the images are stock photography. Does it show a banking product or service in action? Does it offer any additional information about their products? If our attention is primarily drawn to the top of the page, why are we loading that space with filler? We are consistently wasting our reader's attention on large, data-heavy imagery. If these images don't add value for the customer, then we're increasing our carbon footprint with no added information benefit.

When you start to look at these images—really look at them in their context—you start to realize how odd they are. A family portrait for health insurance. A couple looking at a map for auto loans. A mom and little girl nose-to-nose for telehealth services. A close-up of a person in scrubs and a surgical mask for medical software. It starts to become very obvious that the imagery is entirely divorced from the meaning on the page.

None of these data-heavy images contribute to the user experience or their understanding of the product or service. These large images are wasting the valuable space, slowing our reader's progress, using energy, and generating excess emissions.

CONTENT DESIGN: MORE THAN WORDS

I'm going to look at content from the big-picture perspective. It turns out that my mother was right after all: it's not just *what* we say but *how* we say it. If we make information clear, easy to parse, easy to understand, and easy to use, then we are reducing our energy and emissions impact. Conversely, if we have redundancy, unrelated stock art imagery, or poorly structured information, we increase the mental and digital weight for our audience. But poor content presentation isn't limited to digital content. It's rooted in a legacy of terrible information design.

In 2018, my husband had emergency orthopedic surgery after a cycling accident. When he was set free from the hospital the next morning, I was handed a stack of postsurgical discharge papers half an inch thick. The individual pages were all poorly designed, and there was no consideration for the entire package of information: some pages were blurred photocopies of photocopies, others had tiny font sizes, and none were clearly structured. Medication guidelines were scattered over five different pages (sometimes with repeated information); wound care was in three places; and there were several pages of densely packed text about the dangers of narcotic addiction, none of which would have been cognitively processable to someone in acute pain.

I'm a content professional with 25 years of experience working for healthcare companies. I know healthcare content and terminology. Yet I spent an absurd amount of time flipping through the pages, unable to get past *how* the information was structured to be able to find *what* I needed as his caregiver. I was completely and utterly unable to use their information to answer basic questions such as "What medications can/can't be taken together?" or "Is this symptom normal or is it a reason to call the emergency line at 2:00 a.m.?" After the first few hours at home, I gave up on finding anything useful in the discharge papers and did what most Americans do: spent hours seeking information from Dr. Google.

The hospital—a famous and well-regarded medical center—would have benefited from a comprehensive user-centric content strategy and plain language approach to their discharge paperwork, information that could have easily had a customizable patient-specific online option.

Christopher Balmford, an expert in making legal language clear, asserts that calling it "plain language" is not wholly accurate.[14] It's not simply about the choice of words and sentences, but rather the whole document, including language, structure, and design. We often think of these considerations as elements of content design, though I think that the lines between the two are often blurred.

"Content design means not limiting yourself to just words," agrees content strategist Sarah Winters.[15]

"Everything is content," says content strategist Rachel Lovinger.[16] We can't effectively structure the words without considering the layout and organization of the page or screen on which they appear.

In his book, *Plain Language and Ethical Action*, Russell Willerton also talks about plain language as a holistic experience in the context of Healthwise, a company focused on health content and patient education.[17] There are a multitude of factors beyond words that contribute to clarity and comprehension, including:

- Content design and layout, including white space, bullets, boldface text

- The use of images and multimedia to convey complex topics

- The extent to which layout helps readers easily scan info

Is that picture truly worth a thousand words? Can the reader find what they're looking for? "Plain" is often sustainable, accessible, and usable. Let's start by looking at plain language in the context of content design: how the information is arranged to maximize comprehension.

THE WORDS THEMSELVES

Unlike Balmford's definition of plain language as inclusive of structure and layout, the Plain Writing Act of 2010 takes a words-only approach to plain language: "Writing that is clear, concise, well-organized, and follows other best practices appropriate to the subject or field and intended audience."[18] It comes with empathy for the reader.

As Willerton points out, "The common thread . . . for working in plain language is the potential that plain language holds to make situations better for people who need to understand and respond to a message."[19]

There are many definitions for plain language, but there are common threads:

- It represents the needs of the reader.
- It supports comprehension.
- It typically uses fewer words.
- It improves accessibility.
- It makes translation easier.

While some argue that plain language dumbs down the message, it actually improves readability. "It's not dumbing down. It's opening up," explains Sarah Winters in *Content Design*.[20]

Plain language is more than just a good idea. The U.S. government has actual, formalized plain language recommendations based on the Plain Writing Act of 2010.[21]

In *Strategic Writing for UX*, Torrey Podmajersky recommends keeping reading levels below seventh grade (about 13 years old) for general audiences or tenth grade (about 16 years old) for professional audiences.[22] I'd advocate for even lower reading levels in high-stress content:

- Are you writing discharge paperwork for patients who recently had surgery? Keep it simple.

- Are you explaining the terms of a banking agreement? Keep it simple.

- Are you writing a guide for troubleshooting problems with a CT scanner? The technician could be trying to solve the problem on the fly during a disaster or crisis; keep it simple.

- Are you trying to communicate supply chain policies and procedures to a vendor for whom English is not their native language? Keep it simple.

And oh, yes, coincidentally, plain language also reduces page weight, energy needs, and emissions.

Plain, clear, and concise communications sometimes require graphics and imagery. That's okay, even if it increases the page weight and energy use. Why? Because it's adding value for the user in a way that stock imagery can't.

"If you respect your readers, you will make the content work for them," says Winters in *Content Design*.[23] She notes that it doesn't matter where they're coming from or how they find the content. We need to empathize with their needs by making the information simpler, presenting it clearer, and allowing them to find what they need faster. And we do that with plain language.

"Professional ethics involves writing clearly and truthfully," says Willerton.[24] We have an obligation to make our content as clear and usable as possible for all audiences. Too much information floods the working memory and makes it harder to make decisions and complete tasks, even for highly educated audiences.[25] There's really no drawback to plain language. Why would we want to make things harder for readers at any level?

The more pages we have, and the more content on each page, the more complex everything becomes. Usable, functional content helps our audience find answers fast and assess the content's worth, minimizing the number of pages downloaded and data transferred.

LEANER PAGES

As noted in *Sustainable Web Design*, Tom Greenwood points out that roughly half of the weight of a web page is the image file.[26] In most examples of modern web design, that means a large, generic splash image that fills a significant portion of the screen. Not only do those stock art images waste valuable real estate that could be used to draw the audience in, but they're also data heavy and energy intensive.

Data-heavy pages are a bad idea for many reasons. They:

- Slow download times, adversely affecting the user experience
- Tend to waste valuable messaging real estate with stock imagery
- Use extra energy
- Generate more emissions

The more we have on the page, the heavier the page weight. The more weight, the more emissions-generating energy is needed to transfer that weight to thousands of devices.

One of my clients had a very image-intensive home page. It was heavier than the industry average at 5.9 MB and loaded with stock art of healthcare providers doing generic things.[27] Now, I have no objection to imagery—I like a pretty picture as much as the next person—but what value do generic images add for the customer when selling a product or service?

We cut the page weight by half, eliminating many unnecessary images and converting the others to new photos that showed products in action. The images conveyed actual meaning and added context to the user experience. Even with major changes, it was still image-intensive and looked like what you'd expect from modern website design.

We reduced the page weight by 2.95 MB. Multiplied by 1.7 million hits per year, that meant that we avoided the transfer of

4,165 GB of data. Using the metric of 0.81 kWh/GB of data, which I explain in detail in Chapter 3, we avoided 3,374 kWh of energy or 2.6 tons (2.4 metric tons) of greenhouse gas emissions. That's roughly the emissions equivalent of removing a passenger car from the road for six months (Figure 2.2).

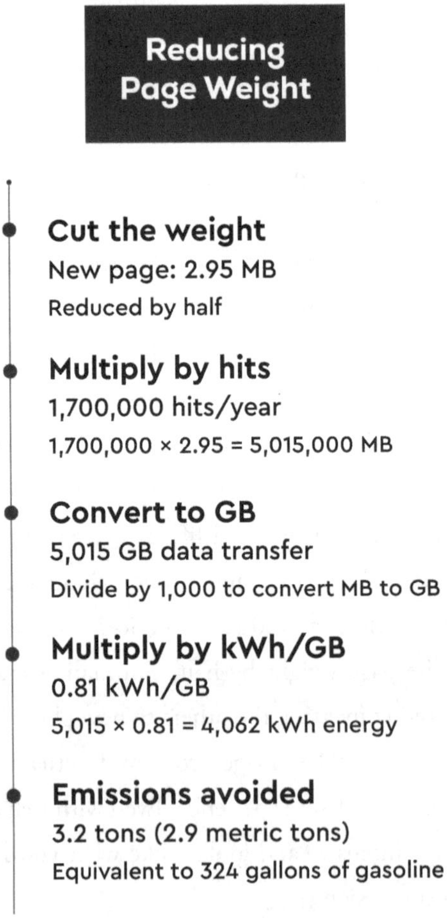

Reducing Page Weight

Cut the weight
New page: 2.95 MB
Reduced by half

Multiply by hits
1,700,000 hits/year
1,700,000 × 2.95 = 5,015,000 MB

Convert to GB
5,015 GB data transfer
Divide by 1,000 to convert MB to GB

Multiply by kWh/GB
0.81 kWh/GB
5,015 × 0.81 = 4,062 kWh energy

Emissions avoided
3.2 tons (2.9 metric tons)
Equivalent to 324 gallons of gasoline

Figure 2.2. 3.2 tons of emissions can be saved by reducing image weight on the home page.

I told that story to my colleague who works at a large financial institution. Their bank drives all traffic to their home page, from their online banking login to their consumer and business marketing. As a result, their home page racks up nearly 400 million hits per year.

Their page size was a relatively small 2.5 MB—not far from what I'd worked my client down to!—but their heaviest element was a generic stock art photo of a woman looking at her mobile phone. Sure, they have a mobile app, but this image didn't show any benefit of the app. She could have just as easily been looking at social media or scrolling through real estate listings.

My colleague shifted the image to a lighter-weight and more relevant image that showed their mobile banking interface instead of "woman with phone" and shaved half a MB off the weight. This seems small until you consider the scope. Multiply 0.5 MB by 400 million hits to see that the transfer of 200,000 GB of data is avoided over the span of a year. At 0.81 kWh/GB of data, that's an energy savings of 162,000 kWh and an emissions reduction of 127 tons (115 metric tons). That's like removing 25 cars from the road for a year (Figure 2.3).

In both examples, reducing the page weight improved download times, presented users with more relevant information, and significantly minimized energy use and emissions. And that's just for the home pages. Imagine that impact extrapolated across a site that has dozens or hundreds of pages.

In many cases, less is more.

Reducing Page Weight

Cut the weight
New page: 0.5 MB
Weight reduced by 20%

Multiply by hits
400,000,000 hits/year
400,000,000 × 0.5 = 200,000,000 MB

Convert to GB
200,000 GB data transfer
Divide by 1,000 to convert MB to GB

Multiply by kWh/GB
0.81 kWh/GB
200,000 × 0.81 = 162,000 kWh energy

Emissions avoided
127 tons (115 metric tons)
Equivalent to removing 25 cars from
the road for a year

Figure 2.3. More hits on a web page means more data transferred.

CLEAR AND CONCISE IS USABLE AND SUSTAINABLE

The beauty of sustainable content is that it shouldn't be more work—it's just a different lens for measuring the impact and value of good quality content. Whether we're considering the design and format of the page or focusing on the clarity of the language itself, we're aligning the needs of the audience and the planet. Accessible, usable, sustainable content adds value not just to the world but also to our careers.

CHAPTER 3

Digital Content's Footprint

The many digital devices and services we use now are made possible through unending exacerbation of economic inequality and the accelerated disfiguring of the earth's biosphere by resource extraction and needless energy consumption.

—JONATHAN CRARY, "The Digital Age Is Destroying Us"

ONE OF THE FAVORITE STORIES in content strategy is the tale of how the U.K. Government Digital Service took 75,000 pages down to 3,000 on gov.uk about a decade ago. Now, web pages were lighter then—about 1 MB per page versus the 4 MB that's more common in corporate pages today. And we don't know the specific traffic data, but I think we can safely make some assumptions.

I think we can very conservatively assume 1,000 hits per page per year as an average, which is only 83 hits per page per month. My defunct cooking blog gets nearly that many, and it's much lower in search results than a government or corporate website would be. In scenarios where information was dispersed across multiple pages, someone might have viewed two, three, or maybe even as many as five pages to find what they were looking for. I deliberately want to use low numbers to show that even without inflationary, magnified data, we're still looking at some significant impacts.

Cutting 72,000 pages at 1 MB per page gives us a starting point of 72,000 MB of data from the site. At 1,000 hits per page per year, we're talking about eliminating 72,000 GB of transferred data. If we multiply that by 0.81 kWh/GB—a number that we discuss shortly—we can see that we've avoided needing 58,320 kWh of energy—that's about 46 tons (41.3 metric tons) of avoided emissions. It's the equivalent of taking nearly nine passenger cars off the road for a year (Figure 3.1).

If they had done nothing and kept those pages—likely adding more as they went because we're all measured by what we create and not what we remove—they would have been contributing at least 460 tons (413 metric tons) of emissions to the atmosphere over the span of a decade.

Strategic planning and effective governance result in digital content that is simpler, clearer, lighter weight, and faster to download: exactly what's needed by both our audience and the planet.

DATA IS ENERGY

Digital content is weirdly intangible. As I remember all too well from my misspent youth working at a dot-com: if you unplug the server, it's inaccessible. Destroy the server and it's gone. Poof!

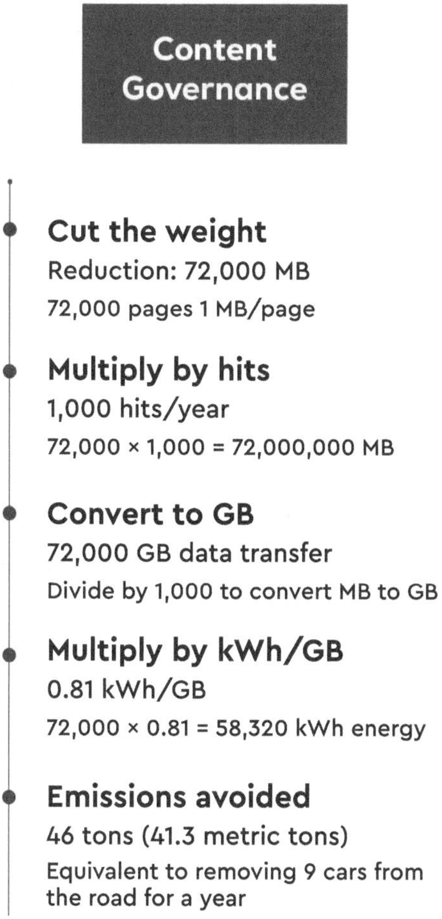

Content Governance

- **Cut the weight**
  Reduction: 72,000 MB
  72,000 pages 1 MB/page

- **Multiply by hits**
  1,000 hits/year
  72,000 × 1,000 = 72,000,000 MB

- **Convert to GB**
  72,000 GB data transfer
  Divide by 1,000 to convert MB to GB

- **Multiply by kWh/GB**
  0.81 kWh/GB
  72,000 × 0.81 = 58,320 kWh energy

- **Emissions avoided**
  46 tons (41.3 metric tons)
  Equivalent to removing 9 cars from
  the road for a year

Figure 3.1. Removing pages can have a significant emissions impact.

Like it never even happened. That's because the bytes that make up our digital content are nothing more than energy. Energy has a carbon cost. We can make direct connections between gigabytes of data transferred and energy use.

Anyone who knows me and knows my love of research rabbit holes will not be surprised to learn that I've spent countless hours researching one seemingly basic question: How many kilowatt hours (kWh) of energy is required to transfer 1 gigabyte (GB) of data? Answers vary from "a lot" to "not much" to "depends on how you measure it." There's a lot of kerfuffle about who says what and what their rationale is. All sources agree on one thing: it's complicated.

Here's what we know:

- Most of the world is using energy that is at least partially generated by fossil fuels, which generates carbon emissions; we need to make some estimates and come up with an average across countries.

- Different devices and different applications draw energy differently, so we need to establish an average across systems.

- Emissions vary based on the intensity of the draw on the energy grid at any given time of day; again, you guessed it, we need to establish an average.

However, we should all be aware that studies and data can reinforce almost any agenda, higher or lower. You may be confronted with different and conflicting mathematical assumptions but know that the underlying principles are sound: data equals energy. Energy equals emissions. Therefore, data has an emissions cost.

SustainableWebDesign.org does a good job of explaining the rationale and research behind their WebsiteCarbon.com calculator.[1] They have settled on a fairly comprehensive number that includes IP core networks and access networks (included in most calculations), plus cables and data centers, as well as the networking equipment and devices in your home or office. That gives them a final number of 0.81 kWh/GB that they use for their calculations, and that's the number we use in this book.

Using the fabulous Greenhouse Gas Equivalencies calculator that's available online from the U.S. Environmental Protection Agency (EPA), I learned that 1 GB of data at 0.81 kWh/GB generates about 1.7 pounds (0.78 kg) of emissions, or about the same as driving a gasoline-powered passenger car 1.9 miles (3 km) (Figure 3.2).

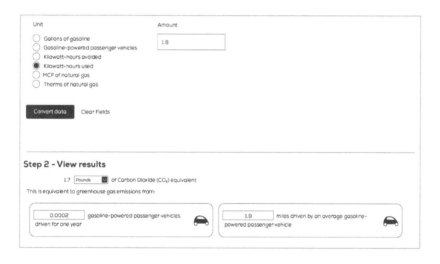

Figure 3.2. The EPA's Greenhouse Gas Equivalencies calculator is an excellent tool for estimating carbon emissions based on energy use. Note: This is U.S.-centric data; the percentage of renewable energy versus fossil fuels varies dramatically from country to country. (Source: Environmental Protection Agency, Greenhouse Gas Equivalencies Calculator, accessed April 10, 2024, https://www.epa.gov/energy/greenhouse-gas-equivalencies-calculator.)

CONTENT COSTS US

It's an oft-quoted statistic that 90 percent of the world's data has been created in the last two years. That's based on research reported in 2013.[2] If anything, the number is higher now. With the rise of social media, we are all content creators, generating data and using energy at an unprecedented rate.

It's little surprise, then, that global internet traffic surged more than 40 percent in 2020, the first year of the pandemic.[3] We were simultaneously streaming video, checking our phones, and navigating Zoom for both ourselves and our school-aged kids. For the first several months, our entire lives were conducted online, awkwardly, as we adapted to our new normal. But as we've returned to some amount of normalcy, our internet-intensive habits remain ingrained. Every bit of it requires energy. And for approximately 80 percent of the energy generated in the United States, that energy creates greenhouse gas emissions.[4]

Our organizations are the places where we have the most leverage. If I, as an individual, become a digital content ascetic—no more streaming video, podcasts, or apps—I'm dramatically altering my leisure time with no measurable change for the planet. If I make a change at a client—reducing file sizes and energy needs for thousands or millions of people—I'm exerting an influence that can result in tons of emissions avoided.

Measuring That App

My iPhone is loaded with apps, some of which bring more value to my life than others. Of course, I used the writing of this book as an opportunity to analyze my collection of apps, measure their weight, and decide whether they were worth keeping.

There are two factors that I consider when weighing an app: the size of the app itself and the amount of data it uses. The following calculations are based on the roughly 70/30 Android/iPhone smartphone marketplace. Where specific Android app size data is unavailable, I've made calculations based on the assumption that Android apps are estimated to be about one-fifth the weight of iOS apps.[5] Let's look at a few common apps (Figure 3.3):

- *Instagram:* It's been reported that there are 2 billion active Instagram users each month;[6] this number doesn't account for inactive app holders or those who downloaded the app and deleted it later, so we know that the downloads actually exceed the numbers that we're using here. Again, as always, I'm minimizing the numbers to show that even in low-end scenarios, we're still looking at significant impact. Estimates say that the Android app is about 30 MB and would have been downloaded by approximately 1.4 billion people. The iPhone app size is 220.4 MB, downloaded 600 million times. This gives totals of 34,020,000 kWh and 107,114,400 kWh, respectively. Together, that's 67,300 tons (61,054 metric tons) of emissions in app downloads, without accounting for use.

- *Venmo:* Assuming that Android is one-fifth the weight of iOS, that gives us estimates of 60 MB for Android and 297 MB for iPhone. There were 70 million unique users of the app in 2021.[7] This means that at least 49 million Android users downloaded the 60 MB app using

2,381,400 kWh of energy, and 21 million iPhone owners used 5,051,970 kWh of energy, resulting in emissions of 3,545 tons (3,216 metric tons) of emissions from app downloads alone.

- *Uber:* There were more than 118 million Uber users in 2021.[8] We'll use the 5 MB Uber Lite app for Android for our calculations (though a larger, more robust Android app does exist), resulting in 334,530 kWh of energy use. On the other hand, the app on my iOS phone shows 302.5 MB, for 8,673,885 kWh of energy use. That leads to 9,008,415 kWh of energy used for app downloads alone, resulting in 4,296 tons (3,897 metric tons) of emissions.

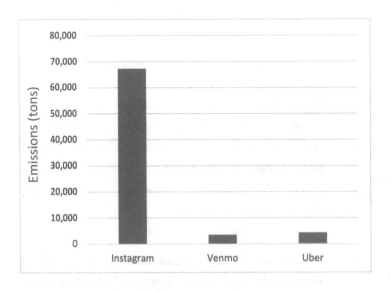

Figure 3.3. App downloads alone have a substantial emissions impact, even before the app is ever used.

Obviously, there are additional emissions that come from the use of these apps. If every active user spends just 15 minutes per day on Instagram, at an estimated 10 MB of data per minute, that works out to a staggering 243 million kWh of energy used and 115,875 tons (105,120 metric tons) of emissions generated each day. That's the equivalent of adding 22,650 gasoline-powered passenger cars to the road for a year.

My Email Inbox Is Already Full

My personal email address, which I've had for more than 25 years, is an absolute disaster. Aside from an abundance of spam, I'm also plagued with emails from every retailer I've ever bought something from since the dawn of the internet. *You should unsubscribe*, you say. And I do! But it's like a game of whack-a-mole: they keep appearing, despite my best efforts.

Do I need another email from anyone? My inbox, groaning under the weight of all that nonsense, says no. What about that email from a streaming provider telling me what's coming soon?

Estimates say that emails are only 75 KB on average.[9] However, there's a big difference between a text-only email about scheduling a meeting and a photo-heavy email newsletter from an airline trying to entice you with a carousel of images of sandy beaches and sunsets. But for the sake of argument, we're going to lowball the corporate emails and use that 75 KB estimate as our standard.

However, "average" is a little misleading in the same way that averaging the net worth of someone in poverty with the net worth of Jeff Bezos (reported as $201.4 billion in April 2024)[10] would mistakenly suggest that everyone is a multibillionaire. We send tons of plain text emails every day, but marketing emails tend to be heavy with imagery and tracking data, increasing their weight.

At that size, each email seems trivial enough. But when we consider that these emails are sent to over 200 million subscribers from a streaming provider, each email blast adds up quickly. That's 15,000 GB of data transferred in each email blast to their subscriber base. At 0.81 kWh/GB, 12,150 kWh of energy is used each week, generating 5.8 tons (5.3 metric tons) of emissions (Figure 3.4).

But remember, these are weekly emails. If we multiply that by 52 to extrapolate over the span of a year, that's the equivalent of adding nearly 59 passenger cars to the road, just for a weekly update about the new season of a show or suggesting that I watch something I've already seen.

And I don't even want to talk about the retailer where I signed up and got 26 image-intensive emails in the span of seven days before I unsubscribed. I can't even fathom what their impact must be.

Say No to NFTs

"I just joined a start-up focused on developing NFTs to build climate awareness," said the woman at the sustainability conference. I don't know if she said more about it because my brain shut down and I started muttering under my breath.

NFTs are shiny, new, and trendy, and even sustainability organizations want to jump on the bandwagon and have their own.

Weight of email
75 KB
200,000,000 emails 75 KB each

Energy transfer
15,000,000 MB
200,000,000 × 0.075 MB

Convert to GB
15,000 GB data transfer
Divide by 1,000 to convert MB to GB

Multiply by kWh/GB
0.81 kWh/GB
15,000 × 0.81 = 12,150 kWh energy

Weekly emissions
5.8 tons (5.3 metric tons)
Equivalent to adding 59 cars to
the road for a year

Figure 3.4. Small emails add up when there are millions of subscribers.

We seem to be ignoring the fact that all indications point to them being a climate nightmare.

NFTs (nonfungible tokens) are unique digital . . . things. It's been described as a sort of next-level fine art collecting, a speculative asset. Digital art is most common, but it could technically be anything digital, like music or books. Much to her confusion, my friend discovered that someone was selling her Substack newsletter as an NFT, so I guess anything goes.

Most NFTs are part of the Ethereum blockchain. Ethereum is a kind of cryptocurrency, and the blockchain tracks who's holding NFTs. (Are you following so far?)

While calculating the carbon cost of a single NFT is really challenging, like many things in sustainability, here's what we do know:

- NFTs are largely bought and sold in exchanges that use Ethereum cryptocurrency.

- There is no oversight of cryptocurrencies. To keep things secure, Ethereum historically required a consensus mechanism achieved by showing proof of work, which involves solving complex math puzzles using energy-intensive computing systems.

- Solving the puzzles earned a new block of verified transactions into the blockchain to gain new tokens.

- The system was deliberately energy intensive and expensive to make it less profitable for someone to mess around and sabotage the system.

- A proof-of-stake update reduced the computational requirements affiliated with proof-of-work systems; this opens the door for long-range or nothing-at-stake attacks that can compromise the system.

As of August 2022, Ethereum was estimated to be using more than 80 terawatt hours (80,000,000,000 kWh) of energy per year.[11] That's roughly the annual energy consumption of Belgium. We can logically infer, then, that anything affiliated with something this energy intensive is not the best use of our resources. While the proof-of-stake update was reported to reduce Ethereum's energy consumption by 99 percent, that would still require 800,000,000 kWh of energy per year—enough to power 9,600,000 light bulbs for a year. An improvement, but still not great.

Long story short: this is probably the single most energy- and emissions-intensive thing your organization can do. Trendy or not, it's best to avoid it entirely.

Video Meetings: Go Dark

Since March 2020, we've spent a significant portion of our days on video calls. Oftentimes we just want to turn our cameras off, but there's an incredible amount of peer pressure or management expectation to be "always on." I'm going to give you a justification for going dark.

Video meetings use data. Data requires energy. Hopefully, by now, we know that energy has a carbon cost. We need to ask ourselves: Did this Zoom call need all 15 of these attendees? Could it have been a phone call instead of video? Even more importantly, could it have been an email instead of a meeting?

When everyone joins the Zoom call (or Teams, or Skype, or Google Meet) with video on, each meeting requires roughly 800 to 900 MB of bandwidth per person. In the past month, I kept track of my meetings. On average, there were five participants per meeting. When everyone has their video on, that works out to an average of 4 GB of data per hour-long call.

That same call—the usual screen sharing, the speaker visible in thumbnail, but other participants in video-off mode—works out to be about 190 MB total on a five-participant call. Leaving everyone's video on for the duration is 20 times as energy and emissions intensive as video off. And let's face it, that's not even taking your personal energy levels into account.

If you're just having a conversational meeting and don't require screen sharing, a 2021 study from the journal *Resources, Conservation and Recycling* estimates that fully video-off meetings have only 4 percent of the carbon emissions of video-on meetings.[12]

Many employers believe that video-on meetings are crucial for building relationships while working remotely. In some cases, I agree. There's no substitute for a face-to-face meeting when you're speaking one-on-one, even if face-to-face is through a screen. But in large group meetings where the grid starts looking like *The Brady Bunch* or *Hollywood Squares*, the value of faces is diminished. A good compromise can be to have video on for the five minutes of meet-and-greet chitchat that always happens at the start of the meeting and then turn video off during screen sharing.

I can't get you out of endless back-to-back meetings entirely, but we can hope that being able to calculate the carbon cost of the video meeting has given you the justification to turn your cameras off.

THE IMPACT OF AUDIO AND VIDEO

In my experience, senior management wants a video as the solution for everything. It's shiny and pretty and can be presented in a meeting to look like we've accomplished something. Everyone feels good about it, and everyone earns their bonuses. Congratulations!

There are times when video is an indispensable tool for walking customers through setup, use, or maintenance of a product or service. There are also times when video is used for video's sake, as we saw in the "pivot to video" trend that was driven by Facebook half a decade ago. In the latter, it is an unnecessary, heavy-weight, flashy example of something that could have been explained just as clearly in text or imagery. Just because management thinks it can be a video doesn't mean it should be.

The email from my longtime client seemed innocent enough. It was a request to put together a series of videos about a specific product line. They were going to be a few minutes long, designed for use in social media, on the website, and at trade shows.

Based on the email, I envisioned these as compelling visual case studies that fit into the larger content strategy that we'd developed the previous year: a complex situation shown in action, a resolution, and an informed user explaining how only ProductName from ThisCo could solve their problem—a video that truly added value for both the audience and the organization.

As I sat in the briefing call, listening to them articulate what they actually wanted, my heart sank. These weren't explanatory, value-add, solution-based videos. The project was simply a feel-good, glossy representation of smiling faces—smiles at the factory, smiles at the whiteboard, smiles in the hallway, smiles exiting the delivery van. The customer was inexplicably absent from the story. The project showed how the company perceived itself as the feel-good hero, without consideration for how anyone else benefited from two minutes of viewing. If the answer to "What is the goal of this project?" is "Because Bob the VP requested it," it's probably not adding value for the customer.

To be fair, it would have been well suited to the trade show floor: limited detail, smiling faces, and uncomplicated narrative stored locally on a hard drive and broadcast on endless repeat. That would have minimal impact in terms of data transfer. The proposed web and social media applications were a different story. There was no value for anyone but management in this project; there was just an emissions cost. But how much cost are we talking about?

Does It Really Need to Be a Video?

Let's look at the size and impact of video in Figure 3.5. A two-minute YouTube HD-quality video has a file size of about 115.2 MB.[13] My client was hoping for 100,000 views of their glossy video across social media, an email marketing campaign, and their website. If they met their click targets, that would amount to 11,520 GB of data transferred. At 0.81 kWh/GB, the video would use 9,331.2 kWh of energy, generating 4.4 tons (4 metric tons) of emissions. That's about the same as driving a passenger car for a year.

But what would the viewer get out of it? Not much. Two minutes of their day lost to rapid-fire cuts of smiling faces and people pointing at screens. Does the happy faces video add value for the customer? Probably not. We're better off investing our time and video production resources in something like a product setup or

Video size
115.2 MB
2-minute video at YouTube HD quality

Energy transfer
11,520,000 hits/year
100,000 × 115.2 MB

Convert to GB
11,520 GB data transfer
Divide by 1,000 to convert MB to GB

Multiply by kWh/GB
0.81 kWh/GB
11,520 × 0.81 = 9,331.2 kWh energy

Weekly emissions
4.4 tons (4 metric tons)
Equivalent to using 454 gallons
of gasoline

Figure 3.5. The glossy two-minute video doesn't add value, but it
adds emissions.

troubleshooting video. It has the same emissions impact, but it has a greater value directly tied to audience needs.

If you're using monetized YouTube content to drive engagement, your videos are probably getting longer. The algorithm favors longer videos that encourage viewers to stay on the platform longer, improving engagement metrics and driving ad revenue. That doesn't mean that longer videos necessarily have more or better information. I think we've all sat through overly long videos that start with an extended splashy intro and lengthy exposition about what we're going to see for several minutes before we even begin to address the actual content.

Obviously, there's only so much you can pad out a corporate product demonstration video for computer hardware or an industrial tool, but what if the content *is* the product? Many creators are uploading videos—from makeup tutorials to unboxing and setup to educational content and live-streamed gaming—that are between 10 minutes to an hour in length.

But what kind of impact do those videos have? I'll select a few at random and round off time and views for easy calculations. All are calculated using estimates from the video file size calculator at toolstud.io. We can see the relative impacts of these types of videos in Figure 3.6.

- TED-Ed videos run about five minutes long, or 288 MB per video. Some of their more popular videos have more than 20 million views. That's 5,760,000 GB of data transferred per video. At 0.81 kWh/GB we can estimate roughly 4,655,600 kWh of energy used for data transfer, or 2,220 tons (2,014 metric tons) of emissions generated—the equivalent of driving 434 passenger cars for a year.

- Sporting events can run for hours. The Milwaukee Brewers and Minnesota Twins game that was streamed as the Major League Baseball game of the week on July 13, 2022, is listed as a featured sporting event on YouTube as I'm writing this (August 26, 2022). The 4.5-hour HD-quality broadcast (15.5 GB) has been viewed 522,000 times. That's used 6,553,710 kWh of energy, contributing more than 3,125 tons (2,835 metric tons) of emissions—the equivalent of driving 611 passenger cars for a year.

- The 12-minute *Vogue* video "24 Hours with Emma Chamberlain in Copenhagen" racked up 2.5 million views in the first eight days. Multiplying 690 MB by 2.5 million gets us a data transfer total of 1,725,000 GB. At 0.81 kWh/GB we can estimate 1,397,250 kWh of energy used, contributing 666 tons (604 metric tons) of emissions—the equivalent of driving 130 passenger cars for a year.

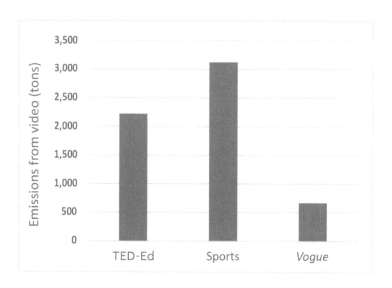

Figure 3.6. While all longer-form videos have a significant emissions impact when downloaded at scale, a full-length sporting event has the largest footprint—like adding 600 cars to the road.

Am I suggesting that we should never create or watch streaming videos? No. Video plays a large role in our lives. But I am hoping this spurs us to consider one very important question before we do: Does this video add value?

Measuring Audio Files

During the pandemic, we moved to a new home more than 700 miles away. Between house hunting and the move itself, we made several seemingly endless road trips. Those 12-hour drives were made slightly more bearable thanks to podcasts. (Shout-out to *The Content Strategy Podcast* from Brain Traffic, *You're Dead to Me* from the BBC, and *Clear and Vivid with Alan Alda* for keeping my nerdy brain entertained.)

One corporate client was releasing an hour-long podcast twice a week, longer and more frequently than average. But most active podcast listeners only spend an average of an hour or less per day listening, time that is spread across multiple shows.[14] Listeners also download more episodes than they listen to, creating a stockpile for offline listening.[15] Every download has an emissions impact.

I'll use the calculator from podcast hosting company Blubrry to estimate the file sizes and relative impacts of different podcasts.[16] It's apparently incredibly difficult to get an accurate independent read on the number of listeners, but some approximate data is available, and as we see in Figure 3.7, the difference in emissions impact can vary greatly.

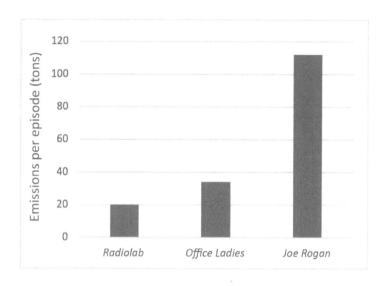

Figure 3.7. The longer the podcast and broader the listenership, the greater the emissions impact.

- *Radiolab:* This popular educational podcast from public radio station WNYC reportedly gets most of its 1.8 million listeners through the podcast versus their live radio broadcast. Let's estimate 1.5 million podcast listeners downloading episodes ranging from 30 minutes to more than an hour. We'll pick 45 minutes at 96 Kbps as the average, for a total of 34.5 MB per episode. That's 51,750 GB of data transferred at 0.81 kWh/GB for a total of 41,918 kWh of energy used, contributing 20 tons (18.1 metric tons) of emissions per episode. That's the equivalent of driving nearly four passenger cars for a year.

- *Office Ladies:* Jenna Fischer (Pam Beesly) and Angela Kinsey (Angela Martin) recap episodes of *The Office.* In

December 2021, they reported 200 million total downloads of episodes of at least an hour in length (45 MB). We can estimate that as of that date, the podcast had transferred 9,000,000 GB of data, which has used 7,290,000 kWh of energy, and contributed about 3,476 tons (3,154 metric tons) of emissions since they launched in 2019. If we average that out to assume an even number of downloads per episode—102 episodes in December 2021—that works out to 34 tons (30.8 metric tons) of emissions per episode or driving nearly seven passenger cars for a year per episode.

- *The Joe Rogan Experience:* The podcast reportedly averages 11 million listeners for episodes that consistently run more than three hours in length (135 MB per episode). That's 1,485,000 GB of data transferred, 1,202,850 kWh of energy, and 574 tons (520 metric tons) of emissions per episode. That's the equivalent of driving 112 passenger cars for a year for each episode.

As with all the communications tools we're discussing, I'm not advocating eliminating any from your repertoire of options. The important thing to remember is to use them efficiently and effectively.

Comparing the Impacts of Audio and Video

"What if we did a video podcast?" asked my client. "It could be like a talk show. Like Merv Griffin."

"Like who?" asked the Gen Z project manager.

"Like Drew Barrymore's show. Or Kelly Clarkson," I said. "But eons ago."

"Oh, I didn't realize they had talk shows back then," she said. And then those of us who had heard of Merv Griffin all crumbled into piles of dust.

I cohosted an early pandemic-lockdown-era how-to-get-through-this-remote-work-thing video podcast with the fabulous strategic business consultant Melissa Breker. Given the circumstances of the time, video made sense. We all spent the first few months glued to our devices as a desperate connection to the outside world, and seeing faces helped. It felt important for the audience to see our expressions and connect with us. But if we were to do something similar today, I would opt for an audio podcast over video because audio has less of an energy draw and emissions impact.

According to the toolstud.io calculator that we're using, a 30-minute video podcast recorded at YouTube quality of 24 frames per second will end up being about 1.73 GB. If we apply the same time parameters to an audio-only podcast, Blubrry estimates that the same content will use about 23 MB of data.

Is it worth 75 times the data and emissions to see my face? Depending on the context, it might be. Video makes sense for virtual conference experiences. Is it a fireside chat conversation for an event? Video will be more engaging. Is it a presentation that requires slides and a talking head to ensure that the message is communicated clearly? Video is the answer. But for conversational discussions like Melissa and I used to have, audio alone makes perfect sense.

Always consider the value of video projects on a case-by-case basis.

THE IMPACT OF DEVICES

Back when I was growing up in the dark ages, all our information came from a single TV, the transistor radio that my mother listened to while doing laundry, and the daily newspaper. That little green radio—playing Phillies games or sports talk radio through AM static—ran seemingly forever on a single little 9-volt battery. Over time, we added my father's record player, a VCR, my bedroom boom box, a massive video camera that used full-size VHS tapes (my mother would go to my high school events looking like a documentary filmmaker), and eventually a desktop computer. But all of that is just a fraction of the devices that operate in my home today, all of which need to be recharged regularly.

We have more content options than ever before, and all of it is digital. From websites to apps, streaming video, music, podcasts, and video conferencing, we spend a significant portion of our days transferring data in one form or another to our phones, tablets, laptops, and TVs. But we'll start with websites, which are undoubtedly the most prevalent digital element of our lives.

We've come a long way since the sparse, text-based sites of the 1990s. (Hello, HTML blink tags!) Today's websites have the visual richness and imagery that was once the exclusive domain of print magazines. We have apps for everything, from tracking our sleep to ordering our groceries and even playing word games. We're able to tweet, text, or otherwise post our images, videos, or text-based thoughts to a variety of social media platforms in seconds, often while multitasking with another device. The rising popularity of the content creator economy has led to a boom in Instagram, YouTube, and TikTok.

Devices Use Energy

Energy transfer alone does not account for the total cost of digital content. Consider the devices that we use to create them. While this book focuses on digital content itself, I would be remiss not to note the significant environmental footprint associated with the manufacture, transport, and operation of any electronic device, including:

- Impacts from mining rare earth minerals
- Waste and pollution associated with the manufacture of semiconductors and other electronic components
- Emissions from the transport of devices
- Energy required for use of the device, even in standby mode
- The waste associated with the disposal of any electronic device

Gerry McGovern talks about these impacts in more detail in his book *World Wide Waste* and on his website.[17] While we won't be addressing those costs in this book, know that every laptop, phone, monitor, server, and modem used by each member of your team amplifies the carbon footprint of your project.

The energy draw of any device varies based on several factors, including the type of device; the age and efficiency of the device; the ancillary devices used with the device, such as computer monitors, Bluetooth keyboards, or wireless headsets; the age and efficiency of the modem; and whether the device is on a wired or wireless connection. We also know from experience that data-intensive activities drain our device batteries more quickly. All of it has an environmental impact.

Calculators do exist to measure cradle-to-grave carbon footprints of our electronic devices. If you'd like to learn more about measuring these impacts, the research by Giovanni Andrés Quintana-Pedraza and colleagues is a good place to start.[18]

Change the Always-On Culture

Are we expecting our teams to be constantly on from the crack of dawn until midnight? Let's stop that nonsense right now.

Ever since the first laptop went home from the office, we've been subject to an always-on culture. The ubiquity of smartphones has made it worse because everyone knows that the ability to check email, texts, and social media is right there in your pocket every night, weekend, and vacation.

I hate to come back to the pandemic again and again, but working from home really blurred the lines between work and life. Normal business hours didn't apply. Time had no real meaning anyway. Emails moved from asynchronous communication that could be handled as needed to something that was increasingly expected to generate an immediate response. As one colleague said to me in 2020, "I feel less like I'm working from home and more like I'm living at work."

I have a radical suggestion: build a work culture where people are truly offline outside of business hours. Encourage your teammates to power down their laptops and phones at night. They might discover that they have more time to truly unwind, go to bed earlier, and approach the morning well rested.

Or, at the very least, they won't find themselves ineffectively multitasking at 10:00 p.m. by streaming a show on their TV, answering emails on their laptop, and checking social media simultaneously. Less energy means fewer emissions. As a former boss once said to me, "Is anyone going to die? Is anyone going to jail? Then that email can wait."

Measuring and Mitigating

If everything we do online has an impact, how can we balance our modern lives and livelihoods with a habitable world? We can reduce our footprint with a handful of relatively easy actions:

- *Replace your devices less frequently:* Maximizing the lifespan of devices reduces the consumption of natural resources associated with mining and manufacturing.

- *Close open tabs:* Open tabs continue to stream data even when idle.

- *Don't cc everyone:* Limit unnecessary data transfer of large attachments by limiting the number of people copied on an email.

- *Send fewer "unnecessary" emails:* A 2019 study showed that 64 million "thank you" or "have a good weekend" emails were sent daily in the U.K., accounting for nearly 26,000 tons of emissions per year.[19]

- *Go to sleep:* Adjust your settings so your computer sleeps when not in use.

- *Better yet, shut it down:* Turn your computer completely off at night.

- *Store data locally instead of in the cloud:* Cloud storage is roughly a million times more energy intensive than local storage.

- *Plug in:* Use a wired connection when available; Wi-Fi uses more energy.

These are relatively small behavioral changes, but they can add up to a significant impact.

THINK BEFORE WE CREATE

I'm not advocating for the blanket elimination of any form of content. I simply want us to create thoughtfully, always keeping the audience's needs in mind.

We can measure the impact of our choices. This isn't additional work. It's simply a different lens for measurement, and it gives us the justification for pushing back when management wants us to generate more, heavier content. It gives us the justification for building governance into our goals, objectives, and bonuses, dedicating valuable time to the thoughtful curation of what we already have rather than the endless creation of more.

And we need to remember to consider the value of the content we create. Let's ask ourselves the following: Does this specific content format add value for the audience? Could this video be audio? Could this audio be text? It's about finding balance between audience needs and the planetary impacts of the many forms of communication that we have at our disposal.

By following best practices and measuring the impacts, we can have a positive impact on the world.

CHAPTER 4

The Looming Impact of AI

Gentlemen, I wouldn't trust this overgrown pile
of microchips any further than I can throw it.

—GENERAL BERINGER, *WarGames*

WHAT ABOUT AI?

If you're in the content industry, you can't be online for five minutes without your inbox, Slack, LinkedIn, and news feed battering you with the latest developments in artificial intelligence (AI). Most are polarized for clicks: it's either the solution to all our problems or the thing that's going to put us out of work.

I am a wildly curious person. I'm forever trying new things and connecting disparate ideas simply because they're there. I don't think that AI is going to save us, and I don't think it's going to result in mass unemployment of content professionals.

I see it from a different angle. AI is a tool. In certain cases— climate modeling or crop yield forecasts or running time-intensive physics simulations for building design—it is basically indistinguishable from magic, allowing researchers to do amazing things with datasets that are beyond the scope of one human's grasp. It excels at information gathering, forecasting, and predictive simulations.[1]

When it comes to content, it's a party trick. Granted, it can be a super cool and fun party trick, but AI is intended to be a tool that solves big, complex, data-driven problems. It's not supposed to power your chatbot so your customers can find the tracking number for their order or generate truly user-centric content. "Mediums, formats, and platforms have changed, but the way humans connect hasn't," says Francesca Rodriguez Sawaya in her Button 2023 keynote.[2]

Using AI for content is like using a Ferrari where you only need a golf cart. Sure, it's cool and powerful, but it's entirely unnecessary and probably wrecks some things along the way.

And, as you probably have guessed, it's really terrible for the climate.

We have established that our digital content has an emissions impact. That is fundamentally an analysis of clicks multiplied by page weight. But what is the difference when the content has been created by AI?

WHAT IS AI?

Many terms fall under the umbrella of AI. I want to clarify them before we go too deep.

- *Artificial intelligence (AI):* the field of study in computer science that develops intelligent machines

- *Machine learning:* the branch of AI focused on developing algorithms that make predictions
- *Large language model (LLM):* an AI algorithm that uses massive data sets to understand and generate content
- *Natural language processing (NLP):* the branch of AI that focuses on giving computers the ability to understand human language
- *Generative AI:* AI that analyzes data patterns to generate new content, including text, audio, imagery, and code (e.g., "Write an explanation of a solar eclipse in iambic pentameter")

So ChatGPT—the best known of the bunch—is a generative AI LLM that uses machine learning and NLP to interpret user queries and generate conversational, understandable responses. ChatGPT is an interface that accesses the GPT data.

However, most people refer to it colloquially as "AI" or "ChatGPT" regardless of the actual underlying system, not unlike the genericization of Kleenex, Xerox, or Band-Aid. That's the terminology that I'm going to use here.

HOW DOES AI WORK?

There are two aspects of AI:

- *Training:* the volumes of datasets that the tool uses to "learn" its skills
- *Inference:* making predictions using the trained models

While significant research is emerging regarding the impacts of AI training, there is less understanding of the impacts of AI inferences. I'll examine them separately here for clarity, but researchers ultimately need to look at the full scope of the process to understand the impact in its entirety. I discuss this more later.

AI AND ENERGY

Even prior to the emergence of ChatGPT, AI was known to be an energy hog. Between 2012 and 2018, the computing power required for machine learning models increased by more than 300,000 times, doubling every 3.4 months.[3] Data centers were consuming more than 2 percent of the world's energy in 2020, and researchers estimated that energy use to increase to "somewhere between 8% (best case) and 21% (expected)" by 2025, according to Amy L. Stein of the University of Florida Levin College of Law.[4]

"With the ever-growing adoption of artificial intelligence (AI)-based systems, the carbon footprint of AI is no longer negligible," write Roberto Verdecchia and colleagues in their 2023 paper "A Systematic Review of Green AI."[5] The growth of AI and cloud-based services is driving record growth in the data center sector, which is being touted as a win for tech.

However, even those who are bullish about data center growth admit to their sustainability drawbacks. "Data centers are massive power users and require significant efforts to keep cool," said Matt Landek, managing director of data centers and telecom at Work Dynamics, in a 2023 press release from commercial real estate and investment management company JLL. "Given hyperscaler and colocation provider sustainability goals, the data center industry will need new innovations to improve cooling and energy efficiency for AI uses."[6]

During Climate Week NYC in 2023, I attended a session on AI and climate. The specifics of that discussion are restricted under Chatham House rules, but I'll give you a broad-strokes summary.

We know that there are energy impacts of data centers, and data storage is relatively low impact until you actively start doing something with the data. In the Climate Week discussion, the panelists talked about how computational demand is skyrocketing as a result of AI.

There are operational efficiencies for AI. Because the system is learning as it goes, it doesn't try to reinvent the wheel every time it's asked a question. This reduces and streamlines large-scale modeling in situations like pharmaceutical drug development or polar ice forecasts. It's less efficient in developing a user journey for selling designer handbags on the internet.

The Climate Week panelists believe AI to be roughly seven times as energy intensive as the standard data center. The nodes are constantly churning at maximum capacity, requiring loads of operational energy and generating heat that requires even more energy for cooling and operational efficiency. And of course, this all has to happen at the cloud level; no single organization could scale the infrastructure needed to build this out themselves.

The obvious question remains: How bad is it?

Like so many things, this is a complicated question to answer. There's legacy data on older technologies, but the pace of growth for AI is rapidly accelerating. Research tends to approach this from the back door: if Company X is developing AI models, and they have publicly reported purchasing a known number of servers or graphics processing units (GPUs), we can estimate the energy draw and related emissions associated with that hardware.

Training: Highly Researched

The training phase is the aspect that's most studied.[7] Processing human language is one of the most energy-intensive uses of AI. Estimates for the impact of training a single model to handle human language are equal to approximately five times the lifetime emissions of the average car in the United States.[8]

One study by Mariarosaria Taddeo and colleagues estimated that a single training run of generative pretrained transformer 3 (GPT-3) produced more than 200,000 kg of emissions, which is roughly equivalent to driving 49 passenger cars for a year.[9] GPT-3 was the predecessor to GPT-4, which provides the backbone of ChatGPT.

But of course, AI researchers don't just train a single model; they often train thousands of models before achieving publishable results. When we see numbers for a single training run or daily energy use, we need to understand that this is just a fraction of the total impact.

Inference: Full of Unknowns

It's easy to think that training is the root of the problem. It's a big problem, to be sure, but it's not the whole story.

A 2023 paper by Alex de Vries looks into the balance of training versus inference and sees signs that the impact of inference may be greater than previously assumed.[10] He looks at a report from research firm SemiAnalysis that suggests that OpenAI required more than 3,600 NVIDIA HGX A100 servers and nearly 29,000 graphics processing units (GPUs) to support ChatGPT.[11] Based on the known energy demand of these components, that suggests an energy demand of 564 MWh of energy use per day. Comparing that to estimates of nearly 1,300 MWh used for a single GPT-3 training run, inference demand has a significant impact (Figure 4.1). Google reported that 60 percent of AI energy consumption stemmed from inference in the period from 2019 to 2021.[12]

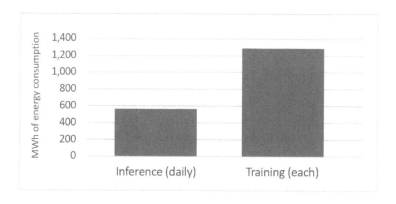

Figure 4.1. The daily energy impact of inferences is about 43 percent of that of training in GPT-3.

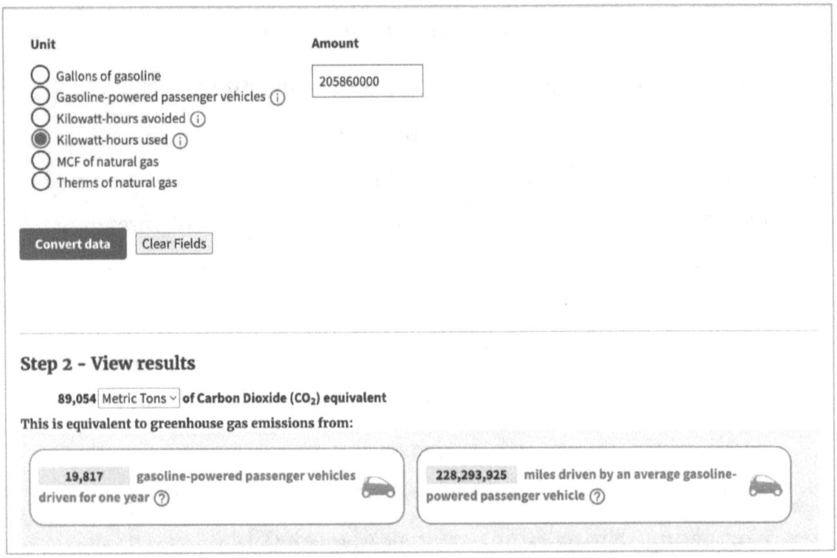

Figure 4.2. In one year, GPT-3 inferences could be generating nearly 90,000 metric tons of emissions.

If we extrapolate this over a year (365 days) and run this data through the Greenhouse Gas Equivalencies calculator, we see that a year's worth of inferences generates nearly 90,000 metric tons of emissions (Figure 4.2). (As a reminder, megawatt hours equal 1,000 kilowatt hours.)

A QUESTION OF ETHICS

I've previously discussed my personal ethical challenges surrounding digital content. I know that this content generates significant emissions, that emissions are driving climate change, and that the effects of climate change are being felt unevenly by the world's most vulnerable populations. This means that I, personally, feel an ethical obligation to influence my clients and mitigate those impacts.

AI brings its own special set of ethical challenges to the party. What if I told you that you could have a shiny new tool to play with, but it was trained on data that was broadly discriminatory and oftentimes copyrighted or proprietary, generated loads of emissions, and frequently offered answers that were inaccurate or contradictory depending on how you query it? Would that sound appealing or appalling?

Discrimination and Bias

A model is only as good as the data it's trained on and the individuals who review it. Training data bias can emerge when systems are designed with poor data sets, reinforcing structural racism.[13] Who was in the room formulating and framing the problem? We blame the data, but this is exacerbated by homogeneous groups reviewing the data for social context, oblivious to the implications and harm.[14]

It's been reported that OpenAI—the parent company behind ChatGPT—hired an outsourcing firm in Kenya to filter the worst violent, harmful, and toxic content for less than $2 USD per hour, which is ethically iffy at best.[15] Yet the problems with content that promotes discrimination, self-harm, and harm to others still persist. My personal favorite headline on the topic comes from CNN: "AI Can Be Racist, Sexist and Creepy. What Should We Do about It?"[16] Unsurprisingly, the article does not solve the problem.

Furthermore, even if we're using "good" data, it can have unintended consequences. Transfer context bias can result when systems designed for one context are incorrectly transferred to another. Interpretation bias is always a possibility, when the user infers something that the designer didn't intend or the system might not support.[17]

Copyright Issues

We know that data used to train ChatGPT was copyrighted or proprietary. Multiple generative AI systems were trained on the Books3 dataset, which includes upward of 200,000 copyrighted books.[18] If you're using AI for your content, you may be generating results that violate copyright law.

Privacy Implications

Even if the model is trained on publicly available data, the question of privacy violations looms large.[19] The information may not be used in the same context as intended. For example, OpenAI stores individual data such as personal information, data which is potentially protected in accordance with the General Data Protection Regulation (GDPR).[20]

How Accurate Is It?

We've probably all seen reported examples of queries that returned incorrect information, known as hallucinations. I don't know about you, but something that's widely known to "hallucinate" (make up answers) does not inspire confidence for me. It's telling you what it thinks you want to hear. I attended a webinar where a content pro for an organization in a regulated industry was using ChatGPT results in their content. I suspect that their legal and regulatory teams are having panic attacks at the revelation.

In 2023, Myeongjun Erik Jang and Thomas Lukasiewicz analyzed the errors and inconsistencies that have appeared in ChatGPT when the same question is phrased differently: "Although LLMs are a revolutionary technique that brought an unprecedented era to NLP, such issues should be resolved before ChatGPT is used in real applications, particularly considering the huge economic and environmental costs for training and inference of LLMs."[21]

BALANCING BENEFIT AND HARM

Even before AI hit the mainstream, digital content was already reported to have roughly the same carbon footprint as the aviation industry.[22] Regional studies also provide aggregate data; for example, in 2014, it was reported that information and communication technology represented between 25 and 33 percent of the electricity consumption of European households.[23] AI is only increasing demand.

Within the industry, there are calls to require transparency with energy and emissions costs explicitly. This would stimulate competition among providers and help everyone understand the true costs.[24] This doesn't even take into account the impacts of mining, hardware manufacturing, and electronic trash. For this, I refer you to the ongoing work of Gerry McGovern, who has done extensive research into the topic.[25]

Fortunately, these questions are also penetrating the mainstream consciousness. "The race to build high-performance, AI-powered search engines is likely to require a dramatic rise in computing power, and with it a massive increase in the amount of energy that tech companies require and the amount of carbon they emit," said Chris Stokel-Walker in a 2023 article for *Wired*.[26]

WHERE DOES THAT LEAVE US?

If we're using AI to get faster and better answers to complex, data-driven questions, that's great. I don't want to wait 20 years to find out how material fatigue affects an artificial knee; I want that modeled upfront. I want researchers to be able to model the cumulative impacts of Amazon deforestation. I want meteorologists to be able to anticipate hurricane intensity and landfall predictions to keep people safe. Yes, these questions will generate carbon emissions, but the benefits outweigh the harms because these questions operate on a scale that's simply too large for humans to calculate manually. But do I need it to run my chatbot? Should it generate product descriptions? I don't think that the benefits outweigh the harms in those cases.

The thing that gives me the greatest anxiety is that we know these impacts, and yet we continue down this path. This isn't like the nascent web with text sites and blink tags. Back then, we couldn't go large with our sites because we didn't have the modem bandwidth to download anything more. But now, our neophilia takes over, and we chase the shiny new tech because we can, without asking if we should.

Let's let humans develop content for humans and leave the high-impact, energy-intensive queries to areas where humans simply aren't equipped to do the work.

CHAPTER 5

Adding Value for Your Organization

At some point in my life I decided, rightly or wrongly,
that there are many situations in this life that I can't do
much about. . . . So what I should do is concentrate
on the situations that my energy can affect.

—JIM HENSON, *It's Not Easy Being Green: And Other Things to Consider*

Now that you know how to correlate content with emissions data, you're probably thinking, so what? Management hasn't really shown an interest in sustainability or content. Why would they care?

There's a saying that I used to hear a lot when working with former U.S. Navy personnel: "What interests my boss fascinates the hell out of me." Your boss is probably most interested in what interests their boss: contributing to the company's bottom line. In other words, it all comes down to money. If you or your department are doing more with less, you have a positive financial story. Of course, when we're solely focused on money, we make short-term and often short-sighted decisions about what does and doesn't matter. But money and sustainability are starting to align.

Why? Because sustainable businesses are more resilient, setting them up for long-term viability and success.

For years, there was the perception that there were businesses that focused on sustainability, like Patagonia, or there were "normal" businesses that put profits first. When I enrolled in a sustainability strategy program at Arizona State University in early 2019, one of my colleagues laughed at me. "You're wasting your money," he said. "What are you going to do, spend the rest of your career working for some hippy-dippy socialist granola company?"

In late 2021, that same colleague pinged me on LinkedIn: "Hey, I was wondering if I could pick your brain about sustainability stuff. It's a real management priority for us now, and I remember that we had a really good talk about it a while back."

The tide has turned. And much to everyone's surprise, the shift is being driven by capitalism.

THE TRIPLE BOTTOM LINE

I'm sure we've all heard about the importance of organizational decisions on the bottom line. Because businesses have historically been focused on this financial bottom line, they chased short-term profits rather than taking a more holistic, long-term approach.

Increasingly, businesses are looking for ways to better balance their operations. They understand that exploitation of employees and the environment might deliver short-term gains, but they also sacrifice long-term opportunities. Balancing people, planet, and profits more or less equally is what's known as the triple bottom line (Figure 5.1).

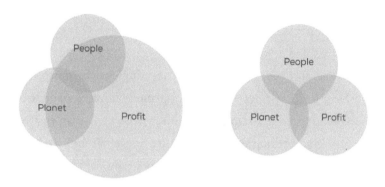

Figure 5.1. The triple bottom line understands that long-term profit can't be achieved without an awareness of the finite resources of people and planet.

The concept was popularized by John Elkington in the 1990s. Elkington realized that looking at things from a straight accounting perspective masked the impacts of capitalism and its future. For example, an organization might look at the direct costs of the water required for their operations but not consider the externalities of how that water use is diverting fresh water from their communities or what happens to the company's blackwater or greywater.

With the triple bottom line, organizations are balancing these elements—or at the very least, not putting all the weight on profits. There is an increasing understanding that planetary and human resources are finite and need to be managed with more care than we've taken in the past.

Is it perfect? No, because businesses are run by people, who are always looking for loopholes. "It was supposed to provoke deeper thinking about capitalism and its future, but many early adopters understood the concept as a balancing act, adopting a trade-off mentality," said Elkington in a *Harvard Business Review* article in 2018.[1]

We've all been in the trade-off meetings when someone is pushing for profit over people and planet. Cap and trade, carbon credits, and net-zero goals are often little more than creative accounting, pushing carbon neutrality and environmental justice to the periphery. If there's a loophole, humans will find a way to exploit it. As Erika Hall writes in a 2018 *Medium* post, "The fundamental challenge we are up against is that doing the right thing well is generally more expensive and time-consuming than doing the least you can get away with and figuring out how to defend it."[2]

So yeah, the triple bottom line isn't perfect, but it's certainly closer to where we need to be than what we started with when I entered the workforce in the 1990s. And as organizations are increasingly measured against ESG targets, I'm hoping for a future where a more balanced approach serves the needs of all stakeholders.

SERVING ALL STAKEHOLDERS

Every organization has stakeholders, which should not be confused with shareholders. For any given organization, stakeholders can include a variety of groups, depending on the type of organization that you work for:

- Employees
- Customers

- Shareholders/prospective investors

- Vendors

- Donors (depending on your organization)

- The communities in which the organization operates

This is a broad population with vastly different needs, but for long-term success, it's important to address all of them.

For me, the three central stakeholder groups are employees, customers, and community. Notice that I didn't mention shareholders or prospective investors. And there's a reason for that! If you're truly addressing the needs of these three primary audiences, you'll be conducting your business responsibly. If you focus too much on shareholders/investors, you're putting too much weight on profits and not enough on people and planet.

Obviously, not all organizations are going to go as far as clothing company Patagonia. In September 2022, company founder Yvon Chouinard announced that he is converting his billions in Patagonia equity to a charitable fund that will invest in environmental conservation.

Charles Conn, chair of Patagonia, explains it as follows: "Investors already look to many company attributes when allocating capital. Over time, the market will continue to work and responsible purpose-led companies will attract more investment, better employees, and deeper customer loyalty."[3]

While Patagonia is an extreme example, others have shared similar sentiments about the importance of serving all stakeholders. "Companies must be deliberate and committed to embracing purpose and serving all stakeholders—your shareholders, customers, employees, and the communities where you operate," said BlackRock CEO Larry Fink in his 2020 letter to CEOs. "In doing so, your company will enjoy greater long-term prosperity, as will investors, workers, and society as a whole."[4]

Let's be clear: I'm not saying that BlackRock has all the answers. They have historically been a financial supporter of fossil fuels, industrial commodity crops, and weapons of mass destruction. However, they are also the largest institutional investor.[5] When they talk about the importance of using sustainability principles to build long-term resilience—yes, in service of a long-term return on investment—companies are going to start listening. But how does that balance equate to long-term business success?

I often talk about Kodak as an organization that didn't balance its stakeholder needs well. On the surface, the business school case study says that Kodak didn't understand where the photography market was headed. It's easy to say that they didn't understand their key stakeholder—their customer.[6]

I'd argue that there was a sustainability element at play. You see, the bigger, lasting Kodak legacy has been the effects of pollution on the Rochester, New York, region. Kodak ignored the community that they were part of. The production of film and photographic paper uses massive quantities of silver. That silver waste built up year by year, decade by decade, with catastrophic impacts on the air, soil, and the ecosystem of the Genesee River.[7] As Kodak lost its commanding market share, it also lost millions in fines and cleanup costs, ultimately filing for bankruptcy about a decade ago.[8]

Keeping an eye on the environment might have saved the Kodak that we knew. But it valued short-term profitability for investors over long-term benefits. If Kodak had built a resilient business that balanced people, planet, and profits, the organization would have seen that business as usual wasn't sustainable. They would have looked for ways to pivot to achieve long-term success.

SUSTAINABILITY CAN BE A RECRUITING TOOL

Employees are also key stakeholders, and increasingly, they want to work for companies that make a difference. Companies that are actively aligning with the SDGs using science-based targets aligned with the Science Based Targets initiative (SBTi). This is in contrast to those that are greenwashing or using marketing spin to make their actions look better than they really are.

According to a 2021 report from Deloitte, "A Call for Accountability and Action," 44 percent of millennials and 49 percent of Gen Z workers have let their personal ethics guide their decisions about the type of work they want to do and the companies they want to work for: "It's not unexpected, then, that millennials and Gen Zs are actively seeking to influence policy and business actions on matters that are important to them, including environmental issues, inequality, and discrimination."[9] All of which, coincidentally, are SDG themes.

"Employee activism is not new," says Deonna Anderson in the 2020 GreenBiz "State of the Profession" report, an annual report looking at corporate sustainability. "But the current rise in activist employees mirrors a trend that has been growing for years, and which seems to be hitting a peak as millennials increase their presence in the workplace. With growing distrust of government institutions, these younger employees are using their voices to advocate for change and demand that their employers do, too."[10]

When we work together, we have workplace leverage.

Prioritizing Sustainability Projects

Salesforce, a cloud-based software company, places a huge focus on sustainability despite its carbon footprint. We know that the cloud is one million times more energy intensive than local storage and is, therefore, a major source of emissions, but businesses aren't going to back away from cloud-based infrastructure. From a strategic business perspective, it makes sense to have a decentralized storage system to connect a global, decentralized workforce.

In a January 2020 blog post, Salesforce talked about why corporate sustainability is important to the organization: it supports alignment with the company's values and goals and strengthens relationships both internally and externally. "We believe these moments create ripple effects—where employees take what they've learned inside the office, and then take it back to their homes and communities."[11]

Sustainability helps Salesforce to do better business and improves the bottom line. They are a good example of a company that looks at sustainability holistically, with awareness of the big picture. There's buy-in at all levels for corporate social responsibility (CSR) initiatives and improvements, and they do an excellent job with both internal and external communications, with sustainability as a core company value that's integrated into every role in the organization.[12] This helps them to effectively recruit within the millennial and Gen Z demographics.[13]

But it's hard to show organizational involvement without CEO buy-in.

The Changing Face of CEO Activism

There was a time, not all that long ago, when CEOs did not voice public opinions on divisive social issues. That's not to say that they didn't hold firm opinions in private, or that they didn't lobby behind the scenes for legislation that benefited their business or personal fortunes. Nobody wanted their CEO to be a polarizing figure, especially with investors.

But in the last few years, there has been a shift toward voicing public opinions on political and social topics. In fact, the 2020 GreenBiz "State of the Profession" report suggests that 43 percent of survey respondents ranked their CEO's involvement in the corporate sustainability program as being "engaged" or "very engaged."[14]

In 2015, as negotiations took place for what would be known as the Paris Agreement, 79 CEOs cosigned an open letter in support of an accord that would have a meaningful, positive impact on climate change.[15] In 2020, more than 200 CEOs announced plans to combat racial inequality and injustice.[16]

If we use Salesforce as the example, CEO Marc Benioff not only supports the organization's sustainability efforts but puts his own money behind ecosystem restoration and climate justice.[17]

As Aaron Chatterji and Michael Toffel pointed out in the *Harvard Business Review* in 2018, the more that CEOs speak up, the more they will be expected to do so.[18] But does CEO activism influence public opinion? *Harvard Business Review*'s research suggests that while the actions of any one CEO don't have a special ability for influence, they can attract media attention— particularly when the issue at hand seems authentic and not directly connected to the company's bottom line.

At the 2022 World Economic Forum in Davos, Switzerland, Benioff noted that the private sector plays a pivotal role in addressing climate change: "I'm ready for a new environmental capitalism. Every company here at the Forum should be net zero and fully renewable."[19]

That's precisely the kind of messaging that attracts the kinds of employees needed for organizations to advance sustainability initiatives and for global progress on the SDGs.[20] But none of these corporate efforts amount to anything without effective communication.

Sustainability Attracts Talent and Investors

One of my clients, who we'll call GenericBrand for NDA purposes, hired a new vice president of sustainability—an outside hire in a newly created role—to develop a strategic and comprehensive sustainability plan. The VP developed a plan to identify improvements or processes that supported the four pillars of reporting: governance, strategy, risk management, and metrics and targets. By aligning each department's efforts with the four pillars, it was easy to identify redundant processes, areas that would benefit from improved collaboration, and areas for improvement.

One of the key areas was communications. The VP unified all aspects of communication under an enterprise-wide communications task force. Marketing, technical communication, help and support, web teams, PR, IR, and HR worked together to develop a sustainability story that put stakeholder needs at the forefront and spoke with a single, unified voice.

Within the first year, the company was positioned as a thought leader. Institutional investors praised the company for its efficiency and resilience, attracting additional capital. Publicity increased the company's profile. HR saw a 10 percent uptick in employee satisfaction (as measured by "I'm proud to work for this company" in surveys). Prospective employees noted that the company's commitment to climate, health, and social justice were top reasons for applying.

Companies like this one will attract more sustainability-minded employees, who will in turn incorporate more sustainability into their workplaces—not as top-down mandates, but through bottom-up initiatives. This, in turn, increases the organization's reputation for sustainability, attracting still more employees who further a sustainability agenda.

SUCCESS THROUGH DIFFERENTIATION

Unlike many aspects of business, sustainability isn't just about keeping pace with the competition. It can be a strategic differentiator. "Companies can gain a competitive advantage by equipping their employees with the skills and knowledge needed to make the most of the opportunities ahead," says the 2018 advocacy report from Business Fights Poverty.[21]

We've been taught that the new systems—clean energy, decarbonization—will have a cost in terms of money, training, and transition. This negative perception stunts behavior change and governmental action. But as technologies are increasingly disrupted, costs and capabilities change dramatically. "No longer is the market a headwind acting against the emergence of a new system, but a tailwind supporting it," say Arbib and Seba in *Rethinking Humanity*, where they discuss their expectations for the social and economic disruption to come. "The challenge is not to overcome market forces but to accelerate and enable them, or at the very least to get out of their way."[22]

We've already noted that renewable energy now costs less than the fossil fuel equivalents. The economic incentives align with doing business better.

External Market Forces Influence Business

Businesses are now the driving force behind sustainable change. Are they doing it out of the goodness of their hearts? In most cases, probably not. But they are doing it. Sometimes the change is driven by employees identifying opportunities for sustainable change.[23] Sometimes it's bowing to pressure from activists, as in the case of PepsiCo and water supplies in India.[24] Deloitte reports that consumers are looking for more sustainable options to support their lifestyles.[25]

Many decisions are driven by the broader global marketplace. The Paris Agreement, for example, required governments to set policies and regulations that reflected each nation's commitments. While the regulations (or lack thereof) out of Washington, D.C., might not have been influencing their choices in the latter half of the 2010s, the decisions made by governmental agencies in Canada, the European Union, or Japan might have. California's more stringent auto emissions guidelines changed the broader landscape; it made sense to incorporate those same standards universally as opposed to selling two different models in California and West Virginia. Technological advances changed automaking across the board. Companies needed to be flexible to adapt to emerging changes.

No matter what governments agree to in global meetings, the World Business Council for Sustainable Development (WBCSD) is acutely aware of the need for business alignment. In their "CEO Guide to the Sustainable Development Goals," the WBCSD says that "this critical [sustainability] agenda cannot be realized without meaningful engagement from business."[26] They published a list of action points for business leaders to follow:

- *Individuals:* Stay informed to ensure that your organization is positioned to capitalize on opportunities and avoid disruptive risks.

- *Companies:* Measure externalities, set goals, develop business solutions, and provide regular and transparent communication of SDG performance and progress.

- *Sectors:* Collaborate with other organizations in your sector to establish industry visions and road maps, and then issue calls to action.

- *Policy-level advocacy:* Openly advocate for the policy and finance enablers that will help achieve a tipping point in sustainability progress.

Put it together, and you have a recipe for business resilience, prepared for disruptions and positioned to be more economically stable.

Business Resilience Attracts Capital

There are two primary aspects to business money. The first is the literal profit and loss of the organization. How can you do your thing more cost effectively and with greater profit margins? But the second aspect is the market capitalization of the business: whether investors are willing to put their money behind your organization. In the 2020s, it looks like investors are looking for businesses that are more resilient to major shocks. Those resilient businesses have often focused on sustainability criteria.

In 2020, during the pandemic downturn, investment funds based on environmental, social, and governance (ESG) criteria showed more resilience. S&P Global Market Intelligence looked at 17 exchange-traded and mutual funds with more than

$250 million in assets that invest based in part on ESG criteria. Of those funds, 14 performed better than the S&P 500 in Q2 2020.[27]

Although 2022 was dismal from a stock market perspective, ESG funds continued to show positive long-term performance. "Over longer time periods, ESG funds have, on average, done well, with 53 percent of U.S. equity ESG funds in the top half of their category," says Katherine Lynch of Morningstar.[28] Taking a different approach to investing may very well lead to more resilient portfolios. Why? Because sustainable, resilient companies have the best prospects for long-term growth.

Institutional investor BlackRock Capital attracted attention early in 2020 with its annual letter from CEO Larry Fink, which he called "a fundamental reshaping of finance."[29] He announced that sustainability would be the foundational standard for BlackRock's future investments.

"Even beyond BlackRock, the rich are getting richer as they reap most of the reward of sustainable investing's growing popularity," said Morningstar in April 2020.[30] In the last few years, global asset manager Nuveen has seen the tide turning toward responsible investing. In their Seventh Annual Responsible Investing Survey, they report that "investors believe that integrating responsible investing principles into investment portfolios plays a significant role in mitigating market volatility."[31] ESG assets exceeded $30 trillion in 2022.[32] By 2023, Morgan Stanley reported that sustainable funds "outperformed their traditional peers across all major asset classes and regions."[33]

"Looking forward, we expect investors to continue demonstrating an appetite to implement these kinds of long-term sustainable investing strategies," said C. D. Baer Pettit, president and COO of research and data firm MSCI on the April 28, 2020, earnings call. "And our research indicates this has been a successful approach during the crisis so far," he added, saying that the company's ESG indexes "have shown resilience even more notably in the first quarter of this year."[34]

How do companies attract the attention of institutional investors and demonstrate the resilience that makes them an attractive investment? Through ESG reporting.

ESG REPORTING

Reporting data is not a new concept for businesses or nongovernmental organizations (NGOs). In both cases, the broader marketplace has long expected these groups to report financial data and produce annual reports that explain the story behind their financials. For example, diminished cash on hand can be explained in an annual report story about the organization's reinvestment in key infrastructure.

Enter sustainability reporting, which is a sibling of traditional financial reporting. More than just a lightning rod for complaints from billionaires, it examines business operations through the lens of sustainability. This type of reporting standardizes and quantifies environmental, social, and governance (ESG) considerations, including costs and benefits, risks, and rewards.

ESG reporting looks at the economic, environmental, and social efforts to quantify the organization's positive or negative impacts on the world. This includes things like greenhouse gas emissions, working conditions, diversity metrics, circularity, and the like—all the things that were covered in the United Nations SDGs. Is the organization contributing to those sustainable development goals or not?

We've crossed the tipping point where it's no longer just a "nice to have" item. It's a valuable resource in the hands of business development and sales. An increasing number of companies require that information when responding to requests for proposal (RFPs), including a major hospital network that requires ESG reporting as part of the submission for new construction projects that are more than five years out. As one of my clients said to me, "If you're not reporting it, it's assumed that you're not doing it."

And it doesn't have to be all rainbows and cotton candy. This isn't a TED Talk, and investors aren't looking for success theater. It just has to be present and grounded in data to prove that the organization is thinking about it and trying to integrate sustainable thinking into strategic business planning.

Taking the effort to report—and implementing the research and strategic processes surrounding reporting—brings sustainability to the forefront of organizational thinking. It ceases to be just an investor relations concern and drives responsibility throughout the organization. Measurement of sustainability considerations then drives the metrics behind departmental goals and objectives.

The reporting process helps call out strengths and weaknesses to influence:

- Vision and strategy
- Management systems

- Employee motivation

- Stakeholder engagement

- Capital inflows

It builds an organization's reputation and trust, identifying competitive advantages and resilience—the kind of resilience that attracts that big-money capital from your large institutional investors. There are a variety of sustainability reports that your company can choose to file.

"But wait!" you say. "If we're trying to compare apples to apples across organizations, shouldn't the standards be . . . well, standardized?" Yes, actually. You're not the first to note that.

"Corporate ESG disclosures lack consistency and standardization," says John Davies in the 2020 GreenBiz "State of the Profession" report.[35] It's been a regular complaint from organizations and investors alike. There are two primary reporting structures: the Global Reporting Initiative (GRI) and the Task Force on Climate-Related Financial Disclosures (TCFD). Both frameworks cover the same sorts of materiality issues, but they approach them differently, making it challenging to align one company's report against another.

In fact, institutional investors like BlackRock have been pushing for more standard standardization in ESG reporting. (Yes, I realize how absurd that sounds.) "BlackRock strongly supports convergence to achieve a globally recognized and adopted approach to comprehensive reporting," the company said in an October 2020 commentary.[36] But in the absence of one unified standard, they're not letting organizations off the hook: they still expect companies to publish both data and context.

The takeaway from this is that for now, there's still no universal right or wrong in reporting. Content is more important than format right now. Everyone is trying to figure it out as they go along. Familiarizing yourself now can help you to get a jump start on something that will be mainstream by the end of the decade.

HOW TO BUILD ESG CAPABILITY

Where do we begin? We can start by figuring out what we're already doing to establish a baseline and measure progress.

Chapters 2 and 3 discuss how to measure our digital communication impacts. These calculations are all scope 3 emissions—a catchall category that includes everything outside of direct emissions and energy purchases—that can be included in our organizations' ESG reporting. These metrics alone put us in a better position to measurably demonstrate our value to management.

If you've already implemented the metrics that we talk about in this book, you're already doing reportable things. Measurable, data-driven stories go a long way in sustainability reporting. Delivering this information to your sustainability person/department, investor or donor relations, or upper management helps them deliver better metrics to all stakeholders, including the institutional investors that drive long-term financial support.

But we're content people, so there's a role for us in helping develop the ESG communications themselves. Putting the creation and maintenance of sustainability tools and reports in the hands of professional communicators will improve outcomes, reduce costs, and directly contribute to the organization's bottom line. Management likes that.

An ESG report is a research-intensive communications project. Management typically approaches it by listing the things that they know they've done: establishing supply chain policies, installing LED bulbs, maybe even purchasing electricity from renewable sources. But they often miss the sustainability story hiding in a financial story.

When starting a fledgling sustainability effort, we start by exploring what we already have and how to make those connections. Take thermostats as an example. Why would an organization buy smart thermostats for their buildings at several times the cost of a regular digital thermostat? Because we've been told that it's going to save the business money in the long run. We're looking at the expenditure in terms of the total cost of ownership.

For decades, we've framed these types of choices in the context of money. But what is a thermostat really saving? Energy, fossil fuels, and greenhouse gas emissions. And if it's reducing energy use, it's reducing the organization's carbon footprint. Most organizations haven't framed it as a sustainability effort. Smart thermostats are a sustainability story hidden under the auspices of money, the story format that we're used to hearing.

But how do we find these stories?

We begin with everyone's favorite process: a content audit. It's highly likely that your sustainability person has never done a content audit. This is why it makes sense for this to be run by content professionals in conjunction with sustainability experts. (Note that while we're specifically looking for those hidden sustainability stories, it's probably a good idea to conduct this in parallel to a broader content audit. Two birds, one stone, and all that.)

Step 1: Conduct a Sustainability-Focused Content Audit

Anyone who has ever moved to a new home understands just how much junk is hiding in plain sight at the old house. It's the same with our content. A content inventory gives us the opportunity to decide what's worth keeping, what's destined for the junk pile, and what can be recycled into something new and useful. A sustainability-focused audit does the same, but through the lens of the SDGs discussed earlier: Do we have stories about benefits to people and planet hiding behind profit?

"The audit helps you identify high-performing content that deserves showcasing," say Mike Atherton and Carrie Hane in *Designing Connected Content*. "It reveals gaps (or opportunities) in which to create new content to better serve the audience. And most often, it exposes a long tail of content that needs a good pruning. . . . The audit exposes your ROT: redundant, outdated, and trivial content."[37]

We're inheriting the archaeological remains of every other content project that came before. If we dig deep enough, we unearth relics of past empires, conflicting information from battling factions, and orphaned projects left in the rubble. But what we also find are SGD alignment and reportable nuggets about how our supply chain policies support living wages and reduced income inequalities (SDGs 8 and 10); programs that support sustainably managed forests (SDG 15); fair trade principles (SDG 12); and diversity, equity, inclusion, and belonging (DEIB) practices that support gender equity (SDG 5). Additional information about what the SDGs encompass can be found in Appendix A.

Step 2: Examine the Content Inventory

The content inventory reveals everything at your disposal—and shouldn't be limited to web content! This includes:

- PDFs
- Images
- Infographics
- Social media
- Printed or online catalogs
- Email campaigns
- Newsletters
- Slide decks
- Videos
- Podcasts
- App content
- Mobile web (if different from desktop web)

This information can be correlated to SEO, metadata, keywords, redirects, and any other metrics about where the information is stored and how it's retrieved by your audience. While none of this is specifically sustainability focused, you'll want to make note of what's where.

There are often lots of surprises when you do a content inventory dig. At one company, we discovered that there were 14 customer-facing undated slide decks on the portal addressing the same topic in different ways; a dozen of these decks were outdated, while the remaining two had been created by departments that clearly didn't speak to each other. How did the customers know what was right? They didn't, and it led to frustration, mistrust, and failure. That's bad news for any content experience, leading to unnecessary downloads, additional emissions, and lost revenue.

Step 3: Analyze the Content

Now that we've opened Pandora's box, we need to assess its worth. Is this stuff any good? Are we saying the right things in the right places to the right people? This is both an overall analysis of how it aligns with our content strategy, as well as identifying what existing info can become sustainability-themed content.

The content analysis is where we look at the quality of what we have. Overall content considerations include:

- Is it consistent with the style guide?
- Is it current?
- Does it reflect current messaging and branding?
- Does it support translation to multiple languages?
- Does it use relevant keywords?

- Is it meta-tagged for searchability?

- Are file naming conventions consistent?

- Does it stand out compared to your competition?

- Does it address your audience's needs or concerns?

Of course, we also need to apply our sustainable content metrics to any of these items to determine what stays and what goes. Are the web pages unnecessarily large? How long is our podcast, and how often are we publishing it? Are our videos adding value for the customer or just for management? We want to ensure that our content maximizes audience benefits while minimizing emissions impacts.

Additionally, as we're documenting what we have, relevant content should be flagged for use by the sustainability department, investor/donor relations, or upper management in their ESG reporting:

- Is a financial story masking a sustainability story?

- What policies and programs are in place to address the social elements of the SDGs?

- What are our requirements for supply chain transparency?

- Are we transporting and packaging our goods efficiently?

- How are we integrating circularity into our products by using recycled materials or ensuring end-of-life recyclability?

This process allows us to examine how the content is structured, researched, and displayed. This is where we uncover how the content does (or doesn't) provide value to our audience on a variety of fronts. Here's where we identify what works—what really works—and sets us apart. Remember, ESG reporting is a differentiator that attracts capital. We need to ensure that our messaging is clear and distinct and addresses the audience's needs. I want to put heavy emphasis on distinct. Do you stand out from the competition, or is your content indistinguishable?

Nearly a decade ago, I did an audit for a client. At the time, they were very much focused on pushing information out to the audience. They were less interested in saying what the customer needed to hear. For a particular product, I took my client's content and stripped out identifying product information and images. I did the same with the competitor's product. Both versions read something like this:

> The Redacted 4000 widgetmaker is the latest in the long line of trusted widgetmakers from Unnamed Co. The lightweight, portable Redacted 4000 is cost effective and easy to use.

> The Unnamed 2000 widgetmaker is lightweight, portable, and easy to use. It's the latest in the trusted line of cost-effective widgetmakers from GenericBrand Co.

I put them side by side on a screen and asked the employees—engineering, product management, attorneys, customer service, marketing, and upper management—to tell me which was the description from their product and which was the description from their competitor's product. More than half of the people in the room guessed incorrectly. But it provided us with a good starting point for everyone to understand that we needed a different approach to truly differentiate the company and support the user journey.

Step 4: Flag for Sustainability

With sustainability communications, we have an extra layer of opportunity in our content audit. What stories do we already have? What have we already been saying in a nondescript way that we can expand on or address differently in a way that matters to our stakeholders? As we see, both Redacted 4000 and Unnamed 2000 tout cost-effectiveness and low total cost of ownership. However, much of those savings came from reductions in energy, chemicals, and water consumption: sustainability stories. Positioned properly, a company could get a head start on the competition by using sustainability as a strategic differentiator. But most companies can't see the forest for the trees.

Step 5: Assign Actions

Working with your internal content departments, begin to assign the actions. Which department should be tasked with a focus on sustainability?

In my experience, it depends on the audience. In some cases, like wastewater, resource management, or pollution, the audience is investor relations. In others, such as where a digital thermostat saves energy and emissions as well as money, it's a marketing and product story. The sustainability department can incorporate all of it into the ESG reports. When sustainability themes are integrated into all aspects of the organization's content, then all stakeholders are aware of the efforts undertaken.

It can also fill a gap in your communications. In the case of Unnamed Co. and GenericBrand Co., it wouldn't have been difficult to differentiate themselves by highlighting the sustainability story underpinning the financial story.

Many customers are already looking at their own ESG stories. Provide them with the information that they need to measure and report the improvements that come from your product or service, or show them how your efforts set your organization apart from the competition.

STAKE YOUR CLAIM

We are still in the Wild West of sustainability, whether we're talking about our own departmental actions with sustainable content, our alignment with business goals for recruiting and resilience, or differentiation through action.

To build the organization's reputation—and of course, attract operational capital—management will increasingly want to see the elevation of sustainability themes in all aspects of our content. While not all organizations are reporting the same ESG information in exactly the same way (yet), that doesn't mean that investors aren't comparing apples and oranges to make sense of what organizations are doing relative to each other.

But to get a comprehensive picture of the scope and effectively communicate what the broader organization is doing, we have to hunt down sustainability stories that are often hiding in plain view as financial stories. The organization has a need for research, analysis, and critical thinking to underpin its sustainability communications, and content professionals have opportunities to identify that content as part of our audits. Being aware of what's needed, how to create it, and how to measure its impacts will put you in a good position for career advancement because sustainability offers long-term returns on investment.

CHAPTER 6

The ROI of
Sustainable Content

If humans are going to make it in the long term,
and preserve our planet along with us, we need
to accept that change is the status quo.

—ANNALEE NEWITZ, *Scatter, Adapt, and Remember*

SUSTAINABILITY STORIES ARE OFTEN HIDING in plain view, both
for the organization and for its customers. One of my clients sells
anesthesia machines, used to sedate you during surgery. When
you breathe in the anesthetic agent—the stuff that knocks you
out—you exhale a surprising amount of it back out. They developed a recirculation system where that exhalation can be recycled
and rebreathed. One midsize medical center saved more than
$100,000 in anesthetic agent costs in one year, which was a great
ROI story.

But look below the surface. Anesthetic agents are powerful
greenhouse gases.[1] If you're using less of the agent, then you're

also emitting less into the atmosphere. It's a sustainability story hiding under the auspices of a financial story.

When we look at sustainable content, it's not a financial driver in and of itself. Sure, we can create less digital content, cull outdated content, and use less space in the data center. But with storage being absurdly cheap these days (you can buy 1 TB of storage on Amazon for less than $50, and AWS cloud storage is less than $25 per terabyte), this isn't what's going to make management take notice. They see the cost of the data sitting there—a direct cost—not the distributed downstream impacts when thousands or millions of people are downloading that content. We need to approach this by articulating the overall value of content and then emphasizing that it has a corollary value as sustainable content.

In the world of sustainability, we often have to find workarounds and backdoors to measure the ROI and savings. We all know that ROI is complicated, but hopefully, these examples of approaches will help you to assess the longer-term value of the content that you provide. No two organizations are the same, so find the metrics that make sense with what you're doing. What we do know is that content is at the center of everything.

SUSTAINABLE CONTENT REQUIRES PEOPLE

Clearly, your content team is fully staffed, has full executive buy-in, and is viewed as a profit center, not a cost center, right? In that case, everything we talk about in Chapter 5 is just upside, a different way to assess your department's awesomeness.

(Colleague enters stage left and whispers in my ear.)

What? Not every organization has a content strategist?

(Whispers.)

Or a content designer?

(Whispers.)

What do you mean that there's only one overextended "content manager" and at least seven different departments are always angling for more digital content?

(Flips table and storms out of the room, mumbling.)

We know that content literally forms the backbone of the customer experience for every product or service out there:

- Introducing the value in marketing and sales

- Offering clear wording and guidance on products and packaging

- Providing information architecture and UX copy for a site or app

- Supporting the user experience with documentation and help

And yet, as we all know too well, we're regarded as a cost center. We spend endless time in meetings pushing back and explaining for the umpteenth time why our content strategy and style guides exist. We fight for a seat at the table when content is an essential part of everything that any organization does. Content should be right in the middle of the room. As Relly Annett-Baker said during her keynote at the Button 2022 conference, we shouldn't be fighting for our seat because "we are the fucking table."[2]

Yet we're the first department to be cut when the economy turns or when a megalomaniac buys a company on a whim. It's bullshit. I know it, and you know it.

Historically, we don't do a great job of demonstrating and justifying the value of content. It's typically seen as a cost center, not a value add. I want to look at how to measure the monetary value, and how that also correlates to sustainability metrics. If we can't justify the existence of the people needed to develop sustainable content and sustainability communications, then we're back to square one.

"Organizations can't create experiences for people without UX content," says the Content Design Manifesto. And we can't create content without people. "Content designers reduce expenses and increase income, impacting metrics for engagement, conversion, adoption, retention, satisfaction, brand affinity, and more. Content designers reduce risk, ensure quality, increase accessibility and inclusion, enable discovery, and affect how people feel."[3]

Understanding the Human Cost of Content

Good, sustainable content doesn't just happen. It needs to be planned, developed, written, and edited by professional communicators. Plural. You can't just hire "the writer" (singular) and call it a day. People cost money. Companies don't like spending money unless they know they can make it up down the line. If you want to justify the headcount to create and maintain good content, you need to know the personnel costs and the ways in which those costs can be recouped.

I'm going to assume that you're understaffed in one area or

another. (Or all areas. This is a judgment-free zone.) Let's talk about HR-type things. In general, in the United States, salary accounts for about 70 percent of an employee's total annual compensation, and a significant amount of the remainder goes to the employer-paid portion of health insurance. (Note: Healthcare costs differ in countries with a functional medical system, but they have other costs like additional vacation days, sick days, parental leave, bonuses, and termination payouts. It's not a one-to-one comparison, but it's close enough.)[4]

Online estimates for the cost of new hires vary widely, with some saying that it's as little as $4,000 to hire a new employee. This seemed low to me, based on the number of hours my teams spent reviewing resumes and interviewing candidates when I worked in-house. So I talked to a friend in HR who outright laughed at the numbers. She estimates that the first year of employment works out to be closer to two times the salary for an office-based employee. How could it be so different? Her estimate includes:

- The cost of inefficiency of a short-staffed department while the role is empty for a quarter or more

- The cost of minimal efficiency for another quarter as the employee ramps up

- HR costs such as recruiters, hourly rates for internal HR personnel, applicant tracking software, background checks, drug screens, and reference checks

- Lost billable hours for interviewers; she estimates 10 to 12 interviewers talking to five applicants across multiple rounds of interviews

- Onboarding and training costs
- Usually a salary bump of 15 percent or more over the previous employee
- Signing bonuses, where applicable
- Increased cost of bonuses as a percentage of the now-higher salary
- Relocation costs, where applicable

I've spent an absurd amount of time quantifying salaries for a variety of content roles and extrapolating them out over five years with 3 percent cost-of-living increases that will likely not correlate to the actual change in cost of living in these inflationary times (Table 6.1). Your first-year costs are the highest, so it works to the company's advantage to keep employees happy for as long as possible. On the flip side, you're looking at a 5 to 10 percent salary bump every time you change jobs, so it's in an employee's best interest to keep moving.

Table 6.1. Cost of acquiring new employees

	YEAR 1	YEAR 2	YEAR 3	YEAR 4	YEAR 5	FIVE-YEAR TOTALS
Content strategist	$200,000	$133,900	$137,917	$142,055	$146,316	$760,188
Content designer	$200,000	$133,900	$137,917	$142,055	$146,316	$760,188
UX writer	$200,000	$133,900	$137,917	$142,055	$146,316	$760,188
Copywriter	$150,000	$100,425	$103,438	$106,541	$109,737	$570,141
Editor	$150,000	$100,425	$103,438	$106,541	$109,737	$570,141
Project manager	$180,000	$120,510	$124,125	$127,849	$131,685	$684,169

Note: These numbers are very much averages; real numbers vary wildly by experience, geography, and industry.

We need these people to make headway in our sustainability efforts, so we need to justify these costs. Let's look at some examples of the business value of content to see how quickly we can pay that off.

Trust Your Strategy

Sustainable content will not cost you extra. It aligns perfectly with things you should already be doing:

- Lighter-weight pages for quick downloads? Sustainable.

- Plain language? Sustainable.

- More relevant imagery (less stock art) that improves accessibility? Sustainable.

Am I aware that this doesn't always happen? All too well.

One of my colleagues, whom I will call Content Sisyphus, told me the story of how their team had to repeatedly push the content best practices rock up the hill. Every time there was a new product (or iteration of a product), the product team and upper management would push for more pages, emails, videos, and podcasts. The management wish list was endless.

Every time, Content Sisyphus had to push back, advocating for the audience and asking, "Does this add value? Does it align with our content strategy, best practices, and business goals?" But everyone else across six product groups was certain that "this time it's different." The content strategy doesn't apply here. Surely, we need more touchpoints, more flair, more *stuff*. So Content

Sisyphus started tracking the sunk time they spent pushing the rock up the hill:

- *Meetings:* Content Sisyphus discovered that they had, on average, two meetings each week per project. Here is the cost of camera-on video meetings for an average of seven participants per meeting:

  - *Financial:* Estimated $52,500/year/project in person-hours, based on average hourly rates per employee

  - *Emissions:* At 5.6 GB data transfer/hour-long meeting, 433 lbs (196 kg)/project per year

- *Slack messages:* Slack was harder to measure, but assuming 15 seconds to read each message (navigate to Slack, read, return to what they were doing), and 30 seconds to craft it. Here is the cost for a Slack channel with an average of 14 participants and an average of 1,500 messages per product launch/update:

  - *Financial:* $7,031/project in person-hours

  - *Emissions:* 2.3 lbs (1 kg)/project

- *Email:* Email had a similar challenge, though the messages were longer and presumably took more time to craft and read:

  - *Financial:* $1,125/project in person-hours

  - *Emissions:* 1.3 lbs (0.58 kg)/project

Extrapolated across half a dozen projects per year, the company was wasting more than $350,000 in lost productivity and generating about 1.3 tons (1.2 metric tons) of emissions. All because the preexisting, agreed-on content strategy was not accepted as gospel.

By tracking these losses, they were able to demonstrate the financial loss and sustainability impacts to management, quantifying the inherent value of following the agreed-on content strategy. Management was surprised to learn the impact, and Content Sisyphus won an innovation award at the quarterly all-hands meeting. Time is money, and money often correlates to emissions. Trust your content strategy.

THE IMPACT ON CUSTOMERS

When a project starts to go off target, I have a habit of asking, "We're putting customers first, right?"

Earlier this year, a product manager fired back with, "Sure, right after we focus on the needs of John in the C-suite."

Getting customers is expensive. Losing them—with the corresponding negative word-of-mouth reviews—is even more costly. How do you retain them? By making the experience efficient, seamless, and usable.

Heavy Pages Lose Business

Heavy pages aren't just environmentally costly. They're also slow to load. Like it or not, web performance *is* the user experience, and how quickly your page loads will affect your search ranking. "People want to be able to find answers to their questions as fast as possible—studies show that people really care about the speed of a page," according to Google.[5]

Technology and cybersecurity company Akamai has set the standard for download times and visitor patience. In 2009, in a study conducted with Forrester Consulting, they declared that consumers expect web pages to load in two seconds and will abandon a site after three seconds.[6] While the data may be old, I don't think we have any reason to believe that humans have become more patient in the intervening years.

In a 2019 white paper on retail best practices, Akamai talked about the speed of web page downloads—and the corresponding speed with which impatient customers will abandon your site. "Faster pages mean a better user experience," the paper notes. "That translates into better conversion rates—and better profitability."[7]

What causes a page to load slowly? Heavy page elements like stock imagery. Pages that are environmentally unfriendly are also frustrating for customers. In the 2019 white paper, Akamai reported that just a one-second increase in download speed decreased conversions by 26 percent.

The Cost of Load Times

Let's look at a retail site to illustrate this. When tested with Pingdom on November 4, 2022, Nordstrom's home page was 8.4 MB and took nearly 4.5 seconds to load. That's more than twice the patience threshold set out by Akamai.

The Pingdom test reveals that most of the Nordstrom page weight—67 percent—comes from images (Figure 6.1). That's

Content size by content type

CONTENT TYPE	PERCENT	SIZE
🖼 Image	67.26%	5.5 MB
📜 Script	28.44%	2.3 MB
𝐀𝐚 Font	1.49%	123.1 KB
📄 HTML	1.35%	111.3 KB
{ } CSS	0.80%	65.6 KB
▶ XHR	0.42%	34.2 KB
▶ other	0.23%	19.2 KB
Total	100.00%	8.2 MB

Request by content type

	PERCENT	
🖼 Image	48.51%	147
📜 Script	29.37%	89
▶ XHR	8.91%	27
{ } CSS	4.29%	13
Total		

Figure 6.1. The Pingdom test identifies the weight of images, scripts, and other page elements.

not surprising for a retailer, but the home page didn't have purchasable product images as much as it had banner ads (such as a "holiday deals" banner) and feel-good images of stylish families or friends enjoying time together. Clicking through didn't take you to that specific dress but to a page of 50 dresses for similar occasions.

Because I like round happy numbers, let's assume that at a two-second download time, Nordstrom gets 1,000 conversions. Following the Akamai guidelines, a three-second download time drops them by 26 percent to 740 conversions, while a four-second download time reduces it to 548 conversions. That's a 45 percent loss of business due to slow page loads.

Conversely, the Akamai data suggests that if they're doing 1,000 conversions at their current page weight and four-second download speed, a two-second load-time decrease should reduce the bailout rate and improve conversions to 1,823—an 82 percent increase over their baseline.

With more than 73 million hits per year, if they could reduce their home page weight by 2 MB, they would also reduce their web emissions by 56.4 tons (51.2 metric tons). Reducing page weight not only reduces carbon emissions but also improves the customer experience, increases conversions, boosts profitability, and makes it more likely that those customers will stick with you. It costs significantly less to retain customers than to acquire them.

It's Cheaper to Keep the Customers You Have

Customers are fickle. In many cases, the only interaction they have with you is through your digital content. Unless you have a monopoly on a given market, if they're not happy, they're going to look elsewhere. (I'm giving side-eye to the one and only internet service provider at my former home in Northern California. You were a special kind of terrible.)

It's often said that customer acquisition costs five times what it takes to retain an existing customer.[8] This is not simply because of the literal costs of acquisition but also because of the ripple effect of dissatisfied customers sharing their negative stories with friends or colleagues or on social media. Conversely, companies benefit from satisfied customers who refer other qualified customers, building the sales and customer pipeline.

U.S. companies lose $136.8 billion each year because of avoidable customer switching.[9] American Express found that 33 percent of customers will consider switching after just one instance of poor customer service.[10] Additionally, 89 percent of businesses see customer experience as a key factor in driving customer loyalty and retention.[11]

Good UX makes customers happy. They get what they need without multiple clicks or calls to customer service. There's a lot of talk about "delighting the customer," but what most customers want is an invisible, seamless experience that's quick and unobtrusive: plain language and lightweight pages that download quickly. In other words, sustainable content.

Increasing customer retention rates by just 5 percent can increase profits by 25 to 95 percent.[12] One customer experience agency found that loyal customers are five times as likely to repurchase and four times as likely to refer a friend.[13] Reducing friction can accelerate the sales cycle and reduce the cost of sales.

What can your organization save if you don't lose dissatisfied customers? Let's use a software subscription model as an example.

- Losing just 100 customers a month at $14.99/month = $116,922/year loss

- Retaining just 25 percent of those customers through good customer service = $29,230.50/year savings

An organization that can reduce friction can reduce customer churn and save money. As we can see, customers are less likely to abandon sites that load quickly. Faster load times generally mean lighter-weight and more environmentally friendly pages.

IMPROVING OPERATIONS

Good content and good UX have operational benefits. If we can improve our content, making it accessible, usable, and sustainable, we have a direct impact on our organization's bottom line.

One of my clients, a multinational medical technology company, was able to cut costs and improve customer satisfaction, giving the financial justification needed to support sustainable content development:

- They reduced text by 50 percent by following principles of content design, and plain language reduced translation costs by $90,000 across nine languages.

- Average time on the site decreased while bounce rates increased—indicating that customers found the answer quickly.

- Call center volume decreased by 38 percent in the first 18 months, indicating that customers were able to find their own answers.

- Customer satisfaction numbers increased from 6.4/10 to 8.1/10 with no other product changes, increasing retention.

Interestingly, the company also saw an uptick in traffic from documentation and help back to the sales and marketing pages. Customers were so pleased with their product experience that they were willing to consider other products from the company: a financial boon that justifies the best practices that align with sustainable content.

Moving to Structured Content

In our less-is-more sustainable content mentality, we can't ignore the benefits of structured content. Structured content is information that is organized predictably and succinctly, tagged with metadata, and ready for use across a variety of platforms. It's also known as COPE: create once, publish everywhere.

This is the "reduce, reuse, recycle" model of content. We're reducing the amount of content that we create in the first place and then reusing and recycling it in a variety of formats. Structured content:

- Is easier to use and maintain
- Reduces duplication
- Allows for reuse
- Simplifies translation
- Improves SEO
- Reduces translation and localization costs

Because the content is consistent, it allows for effective content reuse. It prevents staff from reinventing the wheel every time a new page or resource is created, and it reduces the risk that old content wasn't properly updated. All in all, it supports sustainable content efforts to present information efficiently and effectively.

Help Yourself: Avoiding the Call Center

Poor or inconsistent documentation can have a negative sustainability impact. At one of my new clients, customers reported spending hours trying to find the answers on their own before calling for help. They searched the company's website, read online forums, watched videos, and returned to post in the online forums before picking up the phone. Each web search and video download had a negative sustainability impact.

No one on Earth wants to waste time on hold with the call center. They're already unhappy before they speak to the poor, beleaguered rep. Imagine if the customer had access to well-designed information that followed the principles of plain language to ensure content effectiveness. It would not only reduce service costs but also improve overall customer satisfaction.

As we know, the quality of customer service affects the retention rate. Research shows that 96 percent of customers have stopped giving their business to a company after a poor service experience.[14] Customer retention through high-quality content can have a positive impact on the bottom line. Sustainable content follows the principles of quality content, supporting long-term customer retention.

Plain Language and Compliance

My client, GlobalBrand, was a large, multinational manufacturing company. As with many organizations, they were sending lengthy sustainability policy documents down the supply chain to ensure compliance. The vendors—most of whom were not native English speakers—were struggling to comprehend the lengthy and densely written policy document written in English-language legalese. Management was frustrated: "We need to make sure that our supply chain understands our expectations for sustainability, but Legal won't let us replace or rewrite the policy."

The process began with conversations with the corporate attorneys and supply chain teams to identify areas of improvement. Supply chain leadership wanted to improve clarity, either through plain language or translation. The legal department wanted to maintain an English-only document to ensure that all legal considerations were comprehensively addressed. Both sides felt they had reached an impasse.

To meet these competing needs, a new plain language document structure was developed (Table 6.2). The left column of the document briefly summarized each section in plain language, while the right column retained the full legal text that the attorneys required. The left-column statements were clear and easy to paste into a translation app if there was any question as to the meaning.

The new policy document was issued to suppliers at the start of the year. Nine months later, when the company conducted its next supply chain audit, compliance had improved by 48 percent

Table 6.2. Example of the new policy document structure

SECTION 13.4.2	
We do not tolerate slave labor in our supply chain.	Legalese lorem ipsum dolor sit amet, consectetur adipiscing elit, sed do eiusmod tempor incididunt ut labore et dolore magna aliqua. Ut enim ad minim veniam, quis nostrud exercitation ullamco laboris nisi ut aliquip ex ea commodo consequat. Duis aute irure dolor in reprehenderit in voluptate velit esse cillum dolore eu fugiat nulla pariatur. Excepteur sint occaecat cupidatat non proident, sunt in culpa qui officia deserunt mollit anim id est laborum.

over the previous year. The plain language document simplified GlobalBrand's vetting of vendors and distinguished between language confusion and true noncompliance.

Simplifying the language helped the company align all its systems with the SDGs. They were able to easily identify which vendors were aligning with their goals for labor, equality, waste, energy, and water. They quickly replaced noncompliant vendors, creating a good supply chain sustainability story for stakeholders. Improved content design had a direct impact on the company's operations and compliance with the SDGs.

MEASURING THE VALUE OF CONTENT

Can we improve the world through better content? Yes. I wouldn't be doing any of this if I didn't believe this was true. Professional communicators are going to play some of the most important roles in advancing society over the next decade. But we're going to need some new approaches. We need:

- A solid knowledge of the technical and scientific challenges that we face

- A multidisciplinary sociopolitical understanding of the world around us

- Strong foundations in content strategy, content design, and user experience (UX)

With those tools, we can design better content that allows us to communicate in better ways. But good content doesn't just happen. It needs to be developed strategically—by professional communicators. And if ESG communications are going to play a central role in business, then we—the people who know content inside out and backward—need to help.

In the past five years, sustainability has gone from a sidelined topic to the forefront of corporate communications efforts. Yet, despite the increased importance of sustainability, many organizations still struggle with operational and organizational weaknesses when it comes to putting sustainability communications into practice. What department does sustainability communications fall under? Where is sustainability messaging communicated? Is it solely a reporting consideration, or is it part of the broader communication strategy?

For most organizations, sustainability is relatively new. Metrics and ESG reports were the exclusive domain of "hippy-dippy socialist granola companies," as my colleague pointed out. In the short term, however, the standalone department is where most organizations start.

Sometime in the not-too-distant future, sustainability won't be a standalone department; it will be an integrated part of what happens at every level from accounting to logistics. This is something that has tentacles that reach into every aspect of business. What else is at the center of business? Content. It's a smart career move to get ahead of the curve and understand what's coming.

CHAPTER 7

Sustainability Communications: Challenges and Solutions

You only understand something relative to
something you already understand.

—RICHARD SAUL WURMAN, quoted in Nadine Epstein,
"The God of Understanding"

THERE ARE NO QUICK FIXES for the world we live in. In fact, the
scope of the problem is almost easy to ignore because it's entirely
too massive to contemplate. It's a macro version of staring at a
long to-do list: we're faced with the numbing inability to figure
out how to even take small, progressive actions when the goal
itself is huge and daunting.

"If people perceive there's a threat, they're more likely to
act," says Susan Krenn, former director of the Johns Hopkins

University Center for Communication Programs at the School of Public Health. "But you can raise the threat level so high that people are paralyzed—they don't know what to do."[1] As communicators, we walk a fine line between raising paralytic alarm and enabling action.

But even the most carefully crafted message comes up against our own selfish interests. It's like the Stanford marshmallow experiment played out on a large scale.[2] Humans are not good at delayed gratification. We may know that it takes 713 gallons (2,700 liters) of water to make a single T-shirt, the equivalent of 900 days of drinking water. But do we think about that at the point of sale? Does it factor into our decision-making that we're choosing between drinkable water in 20 years or getting that cheap T-shirt with a pithy comment about wine today?

Both businesses and individuals operate this way: we chase the serotonin bump from treats (individuals) or profits (businesses) without looking at the bigger picture and the broader impacts. "Part of our problem is human nature," says Peter Morville in *Intertwingled*. "We're impatient. We choose immediate gratification and the illusion of efficiency over the longer, harder, but more effective course of action."[3]

He goes on to emphasize points about education and expertise. "Our institutions and mindsets remain stuck in the industrial age. Businesses are designed as machines, staffed by specialists in silos. Each person does their part, but nobody understands the whole."[4] In other words, we act as if we live in our own little waffle square, fenced off from others. It's a sticky situation.

I'm not going to pretend that I have all the answers here. This is huge and complex and has been studied by very smart PhDs, most of whom talk more about the root causes of the problem than about actual solutions. However, I think it's important to understand the *why* behind human behaviors to contextualize the feedback (and oftentimes, the blowback) of wading into these waters.

The ROI information that we discuss in Chapter 6? Yes, that's all absolutely, objectively true: sustainable content aligns with other ROI metrics. It also allows you to work around a climate-dismissive coworker or manager to achieve your sustainability goals without specifically having an argument about climate. As you'll come to see, those people—actively, vocally dismissive—are in the minority. That still doesn't mean that you're willing to pick a fight at work. Understand the psychological reasons for where they're coming from and how to work around those arguments to present outcomes that they'll accept.

WE DON'T ALWAYS ACT IN OUR OWN BEST INTEREST

Whether we're talking about buying an individual T-shirt or the cost of our digital content, we're incentivized to consume more and create more. The true cost of products—the value of natural resources or the impact to the environment—are not factored into the prices that we pay or the metrics that we use at work. It's a systemic issue that doesn't account for externalities.

If we want to take sustainable content to the next level of sustainability communications, we need to understand why these are urgent and polarizing topics, what underpins the human struggle with big-picture thinking, and how to overcome these difficulties to truly communicate and engage.

There are psychological factors at play when we behave contrary to our own self-interest. If the facts are all there, why are these conversations so hard? Precisely because the underlying problems are simply too big for us to wrap our brains around. We're dealing with crises at a scope and pace that humanity has never seen before.

Psychic Numbing: How Huge Numbers Numb Us to Tragedy

The first reason is psychic numbing, a term coined by psychiatrist Robert Jay Lifton.[5] He used the term to describe how people "turn off" feeling in the wake of the unfathomable. The concept has been applied to a variety of threats that are too massive to contemplate: risks of nuclear war in the twentieth century, global financial crises, pandemics, social injustice, and yes, climate change.

Most of us can feel incredible empathy for an individual—our hearts go out to someone who is ill or someone who has experienced tremendous loss. There is an identifiable victim, a clear recipient of our empathy.[6]

But humans are terrible at scaling that response. We can't grasp the scope of the 2022 flooding in Pakistan that left one-third of the country underwater, even if we show that equivalent flooding would cover the landmass of every U.S. state east of the Mississippi River and then some. We would, however, remember our coworker's anxiety about being unable to reach his displaced family in Karachi.

But our capacity for empathy decreases as the number of affected individuals increases.[7] The concept of a single individual resonates personally. We don't even need to know the affected person! But psychic numbing erodes our empathy as catastrophic impacts grow. Paul Slovic, professor of psychology at the University of Oregon notes that "our capacity to feel is limited." Our compassion peaks at one affected individual, begins to decline at two, and continues to collapse until a situation is no longer about individuals but a generalized statistic.[8]

This form of numbing may be psychologically protective, but it leads to apathy and inaction. We simply aren't wired to deal with huge, terrible situations, especially when we're facing several at once. We regularly see this inaction in the context of sustainability. The impact only resonates when it hits close to home, which it will increasingly do.

Knowing this, it's best to ensure that our storytelling hits close to home. There's a reason why nonprofits have long built their fundraising communications on a single child,[9] one specific kind of endangered wildlife,[10] or how famine affects one particular family.[11] Can we highlight a single family? A local business? A familiar nearby region? Their own family or well-being? Where can we make a connection?

Affect Heuristics: Trusting Intuition May Lead Us Astray

Welcome to the world of gut instinct.

Researchers understand that risk can be looked at in two ways:

1. Risk-as-analysis, where judgments are influenced by logical reasoning and deliberation

2. Risk-as-feelings, in which we judge risk based on intuitive reactions to danger

Guess which we default to?

The "affect heuristic" explains our tendency to make decisions based on feelings rather than data. This doesn't mean that gut instinct is necessarily a bad thing. It's often a subconscious response to a lifetime of compiled experiences. We learn from those experiences and intuit risks and benefits based on them. "Scientists estimate that about 95 percent of cognition happens below the threshold of conscious thought," says David Dylan Thomas in *Design for Cognitive Bias*.[12] This is important stuff! It helps us assess risk and take shortcuts to prevent constant decision paralysis. But it doesn't always translate from one situation to another.

We experience this every day. After 30 years of driving, I don't consciously think about how to make a stop-or-go determination when the traffic light turns yellow to avoid an accident or how to explain this nuance to my teen driver. Decades of cooking have given me the experience to intuit when the steak will be ready to avoid ruining an expensive cut of meat or how to balance the fine line between onions that are caramelized and burned. The affect heuristic gives us a useful shortcut in day-to-day life. But it doesn't do a thing for us in terms of new experiences; none of this prepares me to ride a horse or rappel into a canyon.

It also works against us for big, existential threats. In early 2020, most of us did not have personal, lived experience with climate change or pandemics and therefore had no emotional memory of how to respond to these scenarios. It's one thing to say, "I understand that climate change exists" or "I understand that viruses are contagious and dangerous." It wasn't in our mental playbook to understand the need for long-term behavior change as a result of things that we haven't experienced before.

We make decisions based on what feels right in the now, not necessarily what makes sense in the bigger picture. It's one thing to know and accept that climate change is happening in the broader sense; it's an entirely different thing to connect our behaviors to a slow-moving disaster at a planetary scale. Connecting my website or your podcast to climate change seems wildly far-fetched. How could this one seemingly innocuous thing within my sphere of influence cause ripples that affect the entire planet?

Even if we know deep down that something has a broader impact, we still live in a society that rewards and encourages consumption and creation. If we want to drive behavioral change, we need to connect the impact to now. Does a desired long-term behavior change have opportunities that we can draw attention to today? Can we create scenarios that offer immediate benefits?

I think we can safely assume that we all know that litter is bad. We've also heard a lot about the amount of plastic waste in the oceans. Do we know that we shouldn't be leaving plastic waste on our beaches? Of course. Do ordinary recycling bins fix the problem of beach litter? No.

What does? Gamification.

Like many beaches, Malpe Beach in Mangaluru, India, had a problem with plastic waste. Placing regular recycling cans wasn't solving the problem. Enter Yoshi the Fish, a giant fish-shaped metal sculpture that holds plastic waste. Yoshi was designed to bring awareness to how much plastic waste was collected on the beach during a cleanup campaign. A resort in Bali re-created the structure for their beach with a sign that says, "Goby loves plastic. Please feed him!" Suddenly, recycling became a game. People not only disposed of their own plastic waste but collected additional bottles that washed ashore. "Feeding" Goby gave them a serotonin hit that a regular recycling can did not.[13]

Obviously, giant beachfront fish sculptures aren't connected to your content's carbon footprint, but where can you create your own version of Yoshi or Goby? Can you set bonus goals for the lightest-weight page or the best podcast length-to-completion rate ratios? How can you incentivize positive change in a way that brings people on board today?

Confirmation Bias: We See What We Expect

We use our senses to gather information about the world. But because we're so inundated with sensory inputs, we become selective in what we perceive. As I write this, I'm only aware of my thoughts and typing the letters that appear on my screen. I don't notice inputs from other senses, like my hearing or sense of smell. We constantly filter information to prevent our brains from overloading.

Confirmation bias occurs when we see what we expect to see and ignore everything else. We're not going to change our ideas just because someone presents us with new information. If anything, we'll seek out reinforcement for existing beliefs. But why? Some of the reasons overlap with the ideas that we just discussed, but our brains aren't equipped to process the influx of information in the modern, digital world.

Confirmation bias doesn't occur intentionally or consciously. We simply favor ideas that associate and connect with things we already know and understand. For new information to be meaningful to us, it must connect with something we've already experienced.

A colleague from state government was talking with a group of farmers about climate readiness: how to prepare for the storms, droughts, and infrastructure disruptions that will accompany climate change. One of the farmers stood up and loudly denied the existence of climate change. Yet a few moments later he was musing aloud about how he didn't remember such wild weather events in his childhood and how weird it was that they had experienced multiple floods, derechos, and droughts in the last decade.

It would have been very easy for her to scream, "That's climate change!" in utter frustration. However, she took a deep breath and recalibrated her approach. She stopped using the word *climate*—a word that caused him to immediately shut down—and talked about preparing for weather events. Could he change his crops to something more drought-tolerant? Could he prepare his land to have better drainage in the event of intense rains? By meeting him where he was, she was able to connect with ideas that he understood and accepted to achieve both of their goals: preparing for the next disruptive event.

Pluralistic Ignorance: The Spiral of Silence

And if that's not enough, we're also up against pluralistic ignorance. This is when a "majority" opinion deceives others into falsely believing that few people share their opinion. This leads to a spiral of silence in which individuals keep their "minority" opinions to themselves to avoid confrontation.

We see this quite a bit when it comes to climate change. While studies show that most Americans believe in and are concerned about climate change, a vocal minority—with voices amplified by journalists attempting to provide "balanced" coverage—leads us to believe that their numbers are greater than they actually are. This makes the majority reluctant to raise the topic at work for fear of confrontation. "Research suggests that many of those who are concerned about climate change self-silence on the issue, electing not to engage in interpersonal discourse about the topic despite their perception that the topic is important," say researchers in a paper published in the *Journal of Environmental Psychology*.[14]

But the perspective on climate is not black and white, or evenly split. The Yale Program on Climate Change Communication says that there are "six Americas" in terms of perspectives on climate change, on a spectrum from "alarmed" to "dismissive" (Figure 7.1). The good news is that more than half of Americans

Figure 7.1. The "Six Americas" survey shows that the majority of Americans are concerned about climate change, contrary to popular belief. (Source: Yale Program on Climate Change Communication, "Global Warming's Six Americas," accessed April 10, 2024, https://climatecommunication.yale.edu/about/projects/global-warmings-six-americas/.)

describe themselves as "alarmed" or "concerned" about climate change.[15] Yet few report discussing climate change on a regular basis. Why?

About 9 percent of the U.S. population self-reports as actively "dismissive" of climate change.[16] But, oh, those 9 percent are vocal, and the media has given them a platform. That vocal minority pushback makes the quiet majority actively consider whether they want to pick that fight. Meanwhile, the vocal minority has an impact on the middle group who could possibly be swayed either way, opening the door for doubt.

We struggle with the false equivalency perception about hearing "both sides" of a story in the media. While science absolutely has uncertainty and is a process of questioning, skepticism, and review, it is disingenuous when a media outlet or social media post puts two experts on TV "debating" climate change. To the nonscience audience, it conveys that there are two equally weighted perspectives.

We're at effectively 100 percent consensus on anthropogenic climate change within the scientific community. What's more, "nearly 9 in 10 Americans believe that we have a moral responsibility to create a safe and healthy climate for ourselves and our children."[17] Yet the majority believes that they hold a minority position because of the media's amplification of denialists. If the denialists did, in fact, hold the majority position, they wouldn't need to shout.

I'm not focusing my attention on the 9 percent who are actively dismissive of climate change and other social challenges. If we give them our time and attention, we're just in a shouting match with a group that has an answer for everything and a solution for nothing. Instead, we want to focus on that middle group and try to move the needle there. I want to move the Overton window—the range of ideas that the public is willing to consider and accept.

I want to take every group but the most dismissive and move them one spot to the left, shifting the perspective toward action and positive change. I want to put my time and efforts and resources behind organizations that shift the focus and normalize sustainability. That's how we're going to make a difference.

We Mean No Harm

When we're talking about any difficult topic, it's easy to dig in our heels with the "I'm smart, you're stupid" dichotomy that our polarized media wants us to believe.

Look, no one—absolutely no one—actively makes choices that they believe will harm themselves or their loved ones. "Bad" choices are based on a different perception of risk. It's easier to make choices that we think are right for us but will have negative consequences for invisible "others" we never meet. But we need to understand that other people are making choices that can have consequences for us.

We want to feel smart, strong, empowered, and in control of our destinies, and everything around us these days—from climate and health to economic fears and educational challenges—leaves us feeling less and less in control. So the human mind wants to respond by digging in and doing nothing, or actively doing the opposite of what we should do in the face of the thing that scares us.

And this is incredibly frustrating for those who are actively engaged in change. Why are we making changes and sacrifices when our neighbor is rolling coal in a massive pickup truck? How can we bridge that gap? Why should one business go out of its way to use reclaimed and recycled materials when the company next door is polluting the watershed without consequence?

Studies by Nathaniel Geiger and colleagues have examined whether interventions can be taken to increase engaged discussions in the hope that more frequent interpersonal discourse can change the course of the national dialogue.[18] The Geiger study suggested that hope-related interventions can help supporters overcome barriers to discourse. It defines hope as a cognitive-motivational process that orients people toward goal-directed behavior. As we saw in the story of the farmer, it requires meeting people where they are to introduce ideas that support action.

Hope requires empowerment. It requires a sense of agency. And it requires meeting people where they are.

HOW TO DRIVE POSITIVE CHANGE

Nobody wakes up in the morning and thinks, "You know, I want to make the world a worse place today." I've spent 25 years working with content strategy and user experience, thinking that I was making things better by creating better content. But my version of "better" was not necessarily sustainable. Once I put the pieces together, I couldn't go back. As in the saying attributed to Maya Angelou, "Do the best you can until you know better. Then when you know better, do better."

The good news is that humans can be persuaded, and we can do that with content. "People don't want information," says Annette Simmons in *The Story Factor*. "They are up to their eyeballs in information. They want *faith*—faith in you, your goals, your success, in the story you tell. It's faith that moves mountains, not facts."[19] We have to make it personal. But how?

How can we influence people in a positive way? It's not with more data or more numbers. What they want is connection. They require context and clarity to accept new information. A policy paper from the New America Foundation shows that graphs have been shown to be more persuasive than text in counteracting disinformation because they're simple, visual, and easily shared through social media. When we make it easy to understand and place it in the context of what we already know, we can influence others.[20]

According to Dr. Natalie Hallinger, a behavioral scientist

and behavioral change advisor, there are four primary principles behind real-world behavior change:[21]

- *Make it relatable:* Brute force is not the path of least resistance. Where do your goals and their goals intersect?

- *Make it desirable:* Everyone wants to be part of the community. Use social norms to drive behavior.

- *Make it contextual:* Actions need immediacy and context to build engagement. Develop calls to action that involve doing something today.

- *Make it easy:* If the infrastructure supports the "right" choice, then it becomes the easy choice—eliminating guesswork or the need for persuasion.

"All choices are ultimately personal choices," explains Simmons. "If you want to influence people's choices you will find that the most powerful form of influence is always personal."[22] Making it personal makes it real.

Ideas Are Like a Virus

We've all become very well acquainted with viruses in recent years. Let's use that as an analogy to describe information that's new or conflicts with long-term behaviors and beliefs.

If we are confronted with an inundating volume of a virus, our immune system responds aggressively, using fevers and respiratory symptoms to attack the invader and get rid of it. The response is dramatic and aggressive.

If we are introduced to a small amount of a virus—such as through a vaccine—our body can recognize the foreign material, process it, develop antibodies, and moderate our response when it's encountered again.

Ideas work the same way. If I present you with a flood of information that challenges your beliefs and experiences, you'll dig in your heels, fight back, and reject it. If, on the other hand, you're exposed to a small tidbit of information that connects to your life experience, you will be more likely to process the idea, integrate it into your worldview, and accept that information. We want to feel like we have some sort of control.

This is why communication is so important. If done correctly, we can emphasize the areas where we, as humans, can take control and drive our futures, rather than having our futures decided for us.

A colleague presented the sustainable content model in a large meeting, only to discover that the project manager was from the vocal 9 percent of the Yale survey. He took a step back, listened to what the project manager was saying, and presented ideas that aligned with things that the PM already accepted:

- Heavy web pages download slowly, affecting the user experience and decreasing conversions; lighter pages are also more sustainable.

- Listeners weren't listening to the entirety of their hour-long podcast; reducing it to 20 or 30 minutes increased engagement while improving sustainability.

- Video product tutorials had too much intro fluff, which viewers skipped over; shorter videos that got directly to the point were more effective and more sustainable.

By presenting sustainability as an added benefit that aligned with existing benefits, it became acceptable to the project manager as a value-add and not a political statement. This made it easier for the VP of sustainability to later gain his support for the ESG report. It wasn't about his politics anymore; it was about touting successes that mattered to management.

Communicating complexity—any kind of complexity—requires thoughtful and clear communication to ensure understanding and ultimately drive action. This is action to advance not only the cause itself but also the organizations that pursue it.

Use Metaphors

Metaphors exist to make topics approachable and relatable. People may not understand that carbon dioxide is a greenhouse gas and that rampant carbon dioxide emissions cause the greenhouse effect. They do, however, understand the concept of a "heat-trapping blanket."

Watch Your Tone

As we know from our content best practices, tone matters. Too aggressive, and audiences will be turned off.

Informal learning methods can reach hundreds of millions of people effectively and efficiently to promote science literacy. This increased awareness can have a huge influence at the community level. "Through use of reasoned conversation, it is possible to shift the science discourse toward socially meaningful and productive discourse," say Nathaniel Geiger and colleagues.[23]

The Power of Story

As Liese Coulter explains in *Communicating Climate Change Information for Decision-Making*, fear-based narratives risk entrenching patterns of inaction. We need positivity, potential, and progress.[24] We get there with stories.

A good story, the kind that we carry with us, must resonate in some way. Unfortunately, that's not how we've historically approached our sustainability storytelling. Take, for example, the impact of climate on communities.

Environmental justice is a story hiding in plain view. "Most news organizations have missed it, devoting what little climate coverage they do primarily to the words and deeds of scientists, politicians, and activists, who are often White and well off, and focusing on such abstract concepts as parts per million of carbon dioxide, instead of the tangible human tragedies climate change is already wreaking in some communities," said Mark Hertsgaard in the *Columbia Journalism Review* in 2020.[25] He's right. Facts and data won't change our minds. Humans are driven by compelling stories.

"It's almost like journalistic negligence," said Kendra Pierre-Louis, a veteran climate reporter at a Talking Shop webinar about racial and environmental justice news coverage. "You're speaking in highly technical terms when the whole reason you're reporting on it is because it has implications for society and humans. And you're leaving that part of the story out."[26] As change accelerates, there will, unfortunately, be more opportunities to show the scope and scale of inequalities.

We need to address the implications rather than the data. But most importantly, we need to move forward and stop pretending that the problems don't exist.

Strong Positive Connections Combat Disinformation

That vocal 9 percent have been sharing a lot of disinformation. The challenge is that if you repeat a lie often enough, it begins to take hold. As it turns out, that's an issue that's hard to overcome.

The illusory truth effect shows how false claims are misremembered as true simply because they're repeated often enough.[27] And because we tend to lock ourselves into echo chambers with the same friends, family, news sources, and social media circles, those claims appear to be universal truths because everyone in our universe believes them.

"The way in which human memory works can make it difficult to address misperceptions," say Brendan Nyhan and Jason Reifler in their policy paper "Misinformation and Fact-Checking: Research Findings from Social Science." They note that "once a piece of information is encoded, it can be very difficult to eliminate its effects on subsequent attitudes and reasoning."[28]

Disinformation campaigns are successful precisely because

they're "sticky." In *Made to Stick*, Chip and Dan Heath say that sticky ideas make the audience:

- Pay attention

- Understand and remember

- Agree/believe

- Care

- Be able to act on it[29]

"Society as a whole suffers from bad decisions and anxiety caused by misinformation, disinformation, filter failure, and information illiteracy," says Peter Morville in *Intertwingled*. "We can't expect technology to save the day."[30] Properly used, technology can facilitate conversation, but often, it makes disinformation worse.

We need to break through the noise to communicate our message. We can only do that with a solid understanding of the psychological reasons for why we're not hearing it in the first place.

HOW TO DRIVE POSITIVE CHANGE

In a 2013 study published in *Ecopsychology*, survey participants reported that they constantly modified the content of their message to prevent audiences from disengaging based on fear or anger. They found that study participants preferred to have a preliminary understanding of their audience before providing information that could cause confrontation with denialists. "Meeting them where they are is crucial to the success of all the climate change messaging."[31]

"Think about your audience," says Margaret Robertson in *Communicating Sustainability.* "Think about their values and interests and ask yourself why they should care about what you are saying."[32] Good content builds connections between people and their ideas. We want our content to build trust, speak clearly, and help our audience find what they need.

- *Respect your audience's needs, pains, and concerns:* These needs may change over time. Don't expect that what you identified as their need in 2015 is the same as what they'll need in 2025. Keep asking questions. Do the research. Grow and evolve with them. And communicate with them in plain language that mirrors their terminology. For example, if you're trying to attract public health searches during the pandemic, you'll draw a wider SEO audience with "shortness of breath" than if you refer to the condition by the medical term "dyspnea."

- *Listen:* How do you know what your audience needs? By listening or researching. While personas were once thought of as a composite representation of your target audience— "Jane is a White, suburban mother of two"—it's often more effective to create a broad range of stakeholder personas. You may have detractors or deniers who will actively disagree with your ideas or positions. You may have influencers who will actively promote them. Some stakeholders only care about money, while others care about ESG considerations. Identify all of them, discover common threads, and look for ways to address their needs.

- *Be ready to engage:* I once had a teacher who said that the key to teaching was knowing that, over the span of the 180-day school year, he had just one or two days in which he really connected with any individual student. "It's my responsibility to meet them where they are when they're ready," he explained, acknowledging that for some of them, what is said today might not click until much later. "I'm here to plant the seeds. It's up to them to cultivate the garden."

As sustainability communicators, we work with people at multiple stages of their mental garden. We may be seed planters. We may be helping them weed out conflicting information. But we may also be providing the information they need to help others tend to their gardens.

- *Tell stories:* In *Made to Stick*, Chip and Dan Heath talk about how to make stories stick in our memory. They recommend that we find the core message, assess why this message isn't being communicated naturally, and communicate in a way that surprises and engages the reader. This is how we deliver lasting impacts.[33]

- *Find an internal champion:* If an idea comes from within a community, it's more likely to be adopted and implemented. The idea has an inherent immunity from rejection.

WHERE DO WE GO FROM HERE?

Communicating sustainability is complex and fraught with a lot of psychological and emotional baggage. Humans are afraid of change, unable to imagine the unimaginable, and hate being wrong.

Shame does not drive positive change. There are many moments where I think back to when my child was in a toddler playgroup. There's a parental tendency to shout "No!" and wag a finger. "We don't do that." Inevitably, the kid would be left crying in frustration. On the other hand, the parents who took the kids aside and explained *why* we don't do that had fewer tears and tantrums and got better behavior. I say this with love: we're all just a bunch of toddlers. It doesn't matter if you're 3, 33, or 83: no one wants to be embarrassed or feel stupid in front of others.

We need to understand why people act the way they do and tell compelling stories that empower and make change seem positive to have ideas take hold. As content professionals, we know how to tell stories that put the audience first and meet them where they are.

The suggestions, calculators, and metrics in this book are designed to be accessible and empowering. They're within the scope of things we already do but allow us to measure the impacts. We already have the tools to make a difference in this world and jobs that give us the opportunity to leverage systems that are bigger than ourselves.

You don't need a PhD in a science-based discipline to make an impact. I know that progress can't happen at all without my help. Or your help. Regardless of your background, there are opportunities to align your time and energy with a sustainable solution that has immediate benefits for the climate and life on Earth.

Conclusion

Ferb, I know what we're gonna do today.

—PHINEAS FLYNN, *Phineas and Ferb*

Thanks for sticking with this until the end. This book is a lot, I know. Believe me, I feel it every day. And with every news story about droughts and fires, storms and floods, melting glaciers and thawing permafrost, I want to curl up in bed, pull the covers over my head, and just ignore everything. The deep dive into the research for this book was overwhelming, but as terrible as everything seems, I still have hope. And I know I'm not alone.

We, the communicators, are at the center of all things sustainability. We're at a tipping point where the Venn diagram of sustainable business objectives, stakeholder expectations, and professional opportunities all intersect with content. With sustainable content and sustainability communications, we can be key players in our organizations' efforts.

As the IPCC report showed, it's going to require all hands on deck to reduce emissions and undo the damage caused by generations of extraction, exploitation, and overuse. The results won't happen overnight, but they need us to start now. It's a journey that we can't take alone. We're all in this together, and we need each other. (I'm getting a very *Lord of the Rings* vibe from this paragraph. Hopefully, we won't have to gather an elf, a troll, and some hobbits and head deep into the fiery depths of Mordor to set things right, but I am absolutely willing to stand by your side on your journey.)

The good news is that we can demonstrate the fact that we're making a difference just by tracking the metrics of the best practices we employ every day. We are uniquely positioned at the intersection of storytelling and metrics, allowing us to simultaneously bring value to our careers, our organizations, and ultimately, our world.

Sustainable content is usable content. It's clear, concise, and compelling. We don't need special permission. We don't need a sustainability-friendly boss. We just need conscientious content strategy, effective content design, and our arsenal of best practices.

And if you want to take this to the next level and really engage with the sustainability team, that's great news! They are overextended and would likely welcome your help. We'll move forward by leveraging our best practices, piggybacking on financial metrics to justify staffing, normalizing sustainability in all aspects of life, and understanding the human reluctance to accept the scope of what's happening.

Sustainability is a communications challenge. This is your time to shine.

Acknowledgments

THE SEED FOR THIS BOOK was planted in 2017 during a lunch with my high school friend Jim. As we sat in a Manhattan restaurant discussing our lives and careers—his in change management, mine in content that increasingly leaned in the direction of sustainability—he said, "You know, this sounds like it would make for a really interesting book." I told him that it was nothing more than a half-baked idea at that point. "A book is nothing more than a half-baked idea, patience, and a good editor," he said. "Write it, and I'll be the first to critique it and then give you a glowing review."

It seems fitting, then, that I was in New York City when I first got word that my book proposal had been accepted. I only wish that Jim had lived to see it, both for his constructive criticism and for the sincere pride that would have glowed through his review. I do know that I wouldn't have written this if he hadn't given me a gentle shove down this path.

Special thanks go to Katel LeDû and Lisa Maria Marquis for writing *You Should Write a Book*, the link to which was dropped into my Slack DMs approximately three dozen times after my Confab keynote.

Jim was right about the value of editors. Thanks go to Roohi Choudhry for being the first set of official eyes on the draft manuscript, Rebecca Logan for editorial oversight, Jeanette Smith for copyedits, and Jessica Easto for the proofread. And of course, many thanks go to the broader team: HaJ Chenzira-Pinnock for bringing me on board, Leah Pierre for project management, Adrian Morgan for design, Tiffany Barrientos in distribution, Rachel High in marketing, and Gwen Cunningham in digital media outreach.

My eternal gratitude goes out to Richard Mannarino, Mary Conquest, Paulo Fernandez, Torrey Podmajersky, Anita Misra-Press, Joyce Peralta, Melanie Mannarino, Natalie Marie Dunbar, Russell Willerton, Laurie McGinley, and Kristina Halvorson for their insights, support, and humor.

My son, who was also one of my early reviewers, had no idea that I would rope him into this project. I thank him for his patience, his insights, and his humor about everything. He's a vastly better storyteller than I am, and I can't wait to see the future that he builds.

Words aren't enough to say what I want to say to my husband. I thank him for helping me to get where I needed to be.

Sustainable Development Goals

ADOPTED BY ALL UNITED NATIONS member states in 2015, the 17 Sustainable Development Goals (SDGs) are "a shared blueprint for peace and prosperity for people and the planet, now and into the future." While many people think of sustainability through only an environmental lens, the goals encompass a variety of topics, including education, equality, economic growth, and of course, environmental concerns.

1. *No poverty:* End poverty in all its forms everywhere.

2. *Zero hunger:* End hunger, achieve food security and improved nutrition, and promote sustainable agriculture.

3. *Good health and well-being:* Ensure healthy lives and promote well-being for all at all ages.

4. *Quality education:* Ensure inclusive and equitable quality education and promote lifelong learning opportunities for all.

5. *Gender equality:* Achieve gender equality and empower all women and girls.

6. *Clean water and sanitation:* Ensure availability and sustainable management of water and sanitation for all.

7. *Affordable and clean energy:* Ensure access to affordable, reliable, sustainable, and modern energy for all.

8. *Decent work and economic growth:* Promote sustained, inclusive, and sustainable economic growth, full and productive employment, and decent work for all.

9. *Industry, innovation, and infrastructure:* Build resilient infrastructure, promote inclusive and sustainable industrialization, and foster innovation.

10. *Reduce inequalities:* Reduce inequality within and among countries.

11. *Sustainable cities and communities:* Make cities and human settlements inclusive, safe, resilient, and sustainable.

12. *Responsible consumption and production:* Ensure sustainable consumption and production patterns.

13. *Climate action:* Take urgent action to combat climate change and its impacts.

14. *Life below water:* Conserve and sustainably use the oceans, seas, and marine resources for sustainable development.

15. *Life on land:* Protect, restore, and promote sustainable use of terrestrial ecosystems, sustainably manage forests, combat desertification, halt and reverse land degradation, and halt biodiversity loss.

16. *Peace, justice, and strong institutions:* Promote peaceful and inclusive societies for sustainable development, provide

access to justice for all, and build effective, accountable, and inclusive institutions at all levels.

17. *Partnerships for the goals:* Strengthen the means of implementation and revitalize the Global Partnership for Sustainable Development.

The full and detailed explanation of the SDGs, including history and plans for implementation, can be found on the United Nations website.[1]

Where Does Energy Come From?

WHEN FOSSIL FUELS (such as petroleum, natural gas, or coal) are burned, they release carbon dioxide into the atmosphere. Carbon dioxide is a greenhouse gas that traps heat in the atmosphere, causing the planet to warm in the same way that a plant greenhouse traps warmth. While some carbon dioxide exists naturally in the atmosphere, the levels of atmospheric carbon have been increasing steadily since the start of the Industrial Revolution.

There are six primary greenhouse gases:

- *Carbon dioxide (CO_2):* This is the primary greenhouse gas emitted by human activities, particularly the burning of fossil fuels. This is the baseline gas by which other emissions are measured, and it accounts for 76 percent of global human-caused emissions.[1]

- *Methane (CH_4):* Methane is emitted by the production and transport of fossil fuels (coal, natural gas, oil), livestock and agriculture, and decay in landfills. It has a shorter atmospheric lifespan but has a global warming potential (GWP) 25 times that of carbon dioxide.[2]

- *Nitrous oxide (N_2O):* Nitrous oxide is a long-lasting by-product of agricultural and industrial activities. It also has medical applications as the laughing gas that you may get at the dentist. It has a GWP 300 times that of carbon dioxide.[3]

- *Hydrofluorocarbons (HFCs):* These are used as refrigerants, aerosol propellants, fire retardants, and medical anesthetics. They act as replacements for the chlorofluorocarbons (CFCs) that were banned in the 1980s to prevent depletion of the ozone layer. This group also includes common inhaled anesthetic agents used during surgery.[4]

- *Perfluorocarbons (PFCs):* PFCs are by-products of aluminum production and semiconductor manufacturing. They have 10,000 times the global warming potential of CO_2.[5]

- *Sulfur hexafluoride (SF_6):* This is the most potent greenhouse gas, with 23,500 times the global warming potential of CO_2. Used in semiconductors, magnesium processing, and as an insulator in electrical transmission equipment, sulfur hexafluoride remains in the atmosphere for 3,200 years.[6]

Most of the world's energy comes from fossil fuels. However, some energy comes from renewable sources. The amount of renewable energy generation varies significantly by country, according to the most current data available in 2022:[7]

- *UK:* 46 percent

- *Germany:* 41 percent

- *China:* 30 percent

- *United States:* 20 percent

- *South Africa:* 6 percent

We are certainly moving toward renewables, but we're not there yet and we're not moving as rapidly as many people think. If the United States increases its renewable energy production by an aggressive 10 percent per year, we won't cross the 50 percent renewable line until 2030, and we won't be fully renewable until 2037 (Figure B.1).

It's important to talk about the misconceptions surrounding where our energy comes from. There's a lot of media attention given to the increase in renewable energy, which gives the impression that the transition to renewables is further along than it is. But another important factor to be aware of is that humanity is using more energy than ever before.

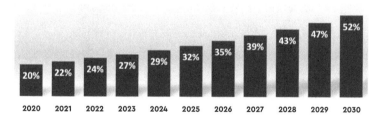

Figure B.1. Forecast percentage of renewable energy in the United States, assuming a 10 percent annual increase.

Our world has nearly doubled its energy consumption in the past four decades. According to Our World in Data, we consumed 88,003 terawatt hours in 1980, a number that jumped to 174,458 terawatt hours in 2019.[8] (One terawatt hour equals one billion kilowatt hours.) "We don't have an energy production crisis," Gerry McGovern wrote in *World Wide Waste*. "We have an energy consumption crisis."[9]

So, as we're increasing our percentage of renewable energy, we're also increasing our total consumption, limiting the amount of headway that we're making on a true green energy transition (Figure B.2). The proliferation of digital communications—from websites to apps, Zoom meetings, streaming video services, and AI tools—has led to an explosive increase in global energy consumption. Our digital content has a carbon cost for every transfer from servers to devices. If we can reduce the energy behind our digital content, we can help mitigate consumption as we drive toward a renewable energy future.

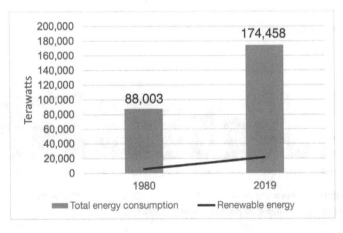

Figure B.2. The increase in renewable energy production is not keeping pace with the increase in overall energy demand.

APPENDIX C

The History of
Climate Regulation

HISTORICALLY, PROGRESS TENDS TO BE DRIVEN by regulation
or formal governance that then had to be backed by hands-on
enforcement. In the last decade—particularly in the United
States—it has been easy to see how the scope of regulations and
protections and corresponding penalties for noncompliance have
ebbed and flowed based on changes in political leadership.

But here's the thing: the planet doesn't care about borders and
governments. Reducing air pollution in Germany will have benefits
for France. Improving the health of the reefs and fish in Palau can
have positive effects on migratory fish populations in the Philippines
or Japan. Conversely, the impacts of deforestation in the Amazon
rainforest don't stop at the borders of Brazil. A pandemic outbreak
in China can upend global public health and economic systems.
Everything everywhere is interconnected.

While many people assume that climate awareness has happened within their lifetimes, we've known about it for more than
150 years. However, governmental agencies and international

efforts toward mitigating climate effects have accelerated in the last 30 years:

- *1856:* U.S. scientist Eunice Newton Foote publishes "Circumstances Affecting the Heat of Sun's Rays," correlating atmospheric carbon dioxide to atmospheric heat retention.

- *1988:* Dr. James Hansen of the NASA Institute for Space Studies testifies before the U.S. Senate Energy and Natural Resources Committee that "global warming has reached a level such that we can ascribe with a high degree of confidence a cause-and-effect relationship between the greenhouse effect and observed warming."[1]

- *1997:* The Kyoto Protocol is adopted to operationalize the United Nations Framework Convention on Climate Change, with the goal of preventing "dangerous" human interference in the climate system.

- *2015:* The Paris Agreement sets nationally determined contributions (NDCs) that limit global warming to below 2°C, and optimistically below 1.5°C. Countries establish an enhanced transparency framework (ETF), similar to ESG reporting but at the national level.

- *2023:* The IPCC AR6 Synthesis Report for Policymakers shows that there is a substantial emissions gap between the existing NDCs and planetary need. Based on modeling, it is likely that we will exceed 1.5°C in the early 2030s and will go well beyond in subsequent decades without significant reductions in greenhouse gas emissions.[2]

While international agreements have been put into place at the governmental level, governments themselves are rarely the source of emissions. The Paris Agreement, for example, sets forth goals, metrics, and reporting methodologies, but governments are only able to influence behavior. There's a disconnect between governmental commitments and corporate behavior. While nations establish guidance and regulation, the amount of that regulation ebbs and flows with changes in political leadership.

Notes

INTRODUCTION

1. Gerry McGovern, *World Wide Waste: How Digital Is Killing Our Planet—and What We Can Do about It* (Gormanston, Ireland: Silver Beach, 2020).

2. Gerry McGovern, Zoom call with the author, April 2020. See also https://www.quarantinebookclub.com.

3. Tom Greenwood, *Sustainable Web Design* (New York: A Book Apart, 2021).

4. Splunk, "The State of Dark Data," accessed May 6, 2024, https://www.splunk.com/en_us/form/the-state-of-dark-data .html.

5. Lucidworks, "The Data That Lies Beneath: A Dark Data Deep Dive," February 17, 2016, https://lucidworks.com/post/ the-data-that-lies-beneath-darkdata/.

6. Eva PenzeyMoog, *Design for Safety* (New York: A Book Apart, 2021), 46.

7. IPCC, "Climate Change 2022: Impacts, Adaptation and Vulnerability," 2022, https://www.ipcc.ch/report/ar6/wg2/.

CHAPTER 1

1. Gerry McGovern, *Transform: A Rebel's Guide for Digital Transformation* (Gormanston, Ireland: Silver Beach, 2016), 10.

2. Liz Coleman, "A Call to Reinvent Liberal Arts Education," TED Talk, February 2009, 18:24, https://www.ted.com/talks/liz_coleman_a_call_to_reinvent_liberal_arts_education?language=en/.

3. Susanne Moser and Lisa Dilling, eds., *Creating a Climate for Change: Communicating Climate Change and Facilitating Social Change* (Cambridge: Cambridge University Press, 2007), 12.

4. Donella Meadows, *Thinking in Systems*, ed. Diana Wright (White River Junction, VT: Chelsea Green, 2008), 5.

5. United Nations Department of Economic and Social Affairs, "The 17 Goals," accessed June 8, 2024, https://sdgs.un.org/goals/.

6. Ucilia Wang, "Lessons from Walmart and UPS on Electrifying Their Fleets," GreenBiz, October 17, 2018, https://www.greenbiz.com/article/lessons-walmart-and-ups-electrifying-their-fleets/.

7. Levi Strauss, "How Levi's Is Saving Water," March 25, 2019, https://www.levistrauss.com/2019/03/25/world-water-day-2019-saving-h2o/.

8. Ariel Cohen, "Corporate Investment in Solar Energy Surges," *Forbes*, July 29, 2019, https://www.forbes.com/sites/arielcohen/2019/07/29/corporate-investment-in-solar-energy-surges/?sh=17d7a0f02464/.

9. Nicolas Kachaner, Jesper Nielsen, Adrian Portafaix, and Florent Rodzko, "The Pandemic Is Heightening Environmental Awareness," Boston Consulting Group, July 14, 2020, https://www.bcg.com/publications/2020/pandemic-is-heightening-environmental-awareness/.

10. National Oceanic and Atmospheric Administration, "2023 Was the World's Warmest Year on Record, by Far," January 12, 2024, https://www.noaa.gov/news/2023-was-worlds-warmest-year-on-record-by-far/.

Notes

11. Inflation Reduction Act of 2022, Public L. No. 117-169, https://www.congress.gov/bill/117th-congress/house-bill/5376/.

12. European Commission, "The Green Deal Industrial Plan: Putting Europe's Net-Zero Industry in the Lead," February 1, 2023, https://ec.europa.eu/commission/presscorner/detail/en/ip_23_510/.

13. Cristianne Close, "The Global Eco-wakening: How Consumers Are Driving Sustainability," World Economic Forum, May 18, 2021, https://www.weforum.org/agenda/2021/05/eco-wakening-consumers-driving-sustainability/.

14. Gabriele C. Hegerl, Francis W. Zwiers, Pascale Braconnot, Nathan P. Gillett, Yong Luo, Jose A. Marengo Orsini, Neville Nicholls, Joyce E. Penner, and Peter A. Stott, "Understanding and Attributing Climate Change," in *Climate Change 2007: The Physical Science Basis* (Cambridge: Cambridge University Press, 2007), 727, https://www.ipcc.ch/site/assets/uploads/2018/02/ar4-wg1-chapter9-1.pdf.

15. UN WomenWatch, "Women, Gender Equality, and Climate Change," 2009, https://www.un.org/womenwatch/feature/climate_change/downloads/Women_and_Climate_Change_Factsheet.pdf; Kim van Daalen, Laura Jung, Roopa Dhatt, and Alexandra L. Phelan, "Climate Change and Gender-Based Health Disparities," *The Lancet* 4, no. 2, (February 2020): 1181.

16. OECD, "Poverty and Climate Change: Reducing the Vulnerability of the Poor through Adaptation," 2002, https://www.oecd.org/env/cc/2502872.pdf; Takahiro Yabe and Satish V. Ukkusuri, "Effects of Income Inequality on Evacuation, Reentry and Segregation after Disasters," *Transportation Research Part D: Transport and Environment* 82 (May 2020), https://doi.org/10.1016/j.trd.2020.102260.

17. United States Environmental Protection Agency, "EPA Report Shows Disproportionate Impacts of Climate Change on Socially Vulnerable Populations in the United States," September 2, 2021, https://www.epa.gov/newsreleases/epa-report-shows -disproportionate-impacts-climate-change-socially-vulnerable/.

18. Yale Program on Climate Change Communication, "Global Warming's Six Americas," accessed June 8, 2024, https://climatecommunication.yale.edu/about/projects/ global-warmings-six-americas/.

19. Hans-O. Pörtner, Debra C. Roberts, Helen Adams, Carolina Adler, Paulina Aldunce, Elham Ali, Rawshan Ara Begum, et al., "Summary for Policymakers," in *Climate Change 2022: Impacts, Adaptation and Vulnerability* (Cambridge: Cambridge University Press, 2022), https://www.ipcc.ch/report/ar6/wg2/downloads/ report/IPCC_AR6_WGII_SummaryForPolicymakers.pdf.

20. Logan A. Bickel and Stephanie D. Preston, "Environmental Impassivity: Blunted Emotionality Undermines Concern for the Environment," *Emotion* 23, no. 4 (June 2023): 1175–1189.

21. Paul Griffin, "The Carbon Majors Database: CDP Carbon Majors Report 2017," CDP, July 2017, https://cdn.cdp.net/ cdp-production/cms/reports/documents/000/002/327/original/ Carbon-Majors-Report-2017.pdf.

22. International Energy Agency, "Net Zero by 2050," 2021, https://www.iea.org/reports/net-zero-by-2050/.

23. Tim Maxwell, "Who Rents and Who Owns in the U.S.?" Experian, October 12, 2022, https://www.experian.com/blogs/ ask-experian/who-rents-and-who-owns-in-united-states/; HOA-USA, "About HOA-USA," accessed April 18, 2024, https://hoa-usa.com/about/.

24. United States Environmental Protection Agency, "Greenhouse Gas Emissions from a Typical Passenger Vehicle," August 28,

2023, https://www.epa.gov/greenvehicles/greenhouse-gas
-emissions-typical-passenger-vehicle/; U.S. Department of
Energy, "Emissions from Electric Vehicles," accessed April 18,
2024, https://afdc.energy.gov/vehicles/electric-emissions/.

25. Sam Meredith, "Private Jet Flights in Europe Soar to Record
Levels—and Most Were Ultra-Short Journeys," CNBC, March
30, 2023, https://www.cnbc.com/2023/03/30/private-jet
-flights-in-europe-soar-to-record-levels-stoking-climate-fears
.html/.

26. International Energy Agency, "Net Zero by 2050."

27. Intergovernmental Panel on Climate Change, "The
Intergovernmental Panel on Climate Change," accessed
April 18, 2024, https://www.ipcc.ch/.

28. James Arbib and Tony Seba, *Rethinking Humanity: Five
Foundational Sector Disruptions, the Lifecycle of Civilizations,
and the Coming Age of Freedom* (RethinkX, 2020), 4.

29. Chris Lafakis, Laura Ratz, Emily Fazio, and Maria Cosma, "The
Economic Implications of Climate Change," Moody's Analytics,
June 2019, https://www.moodysanalytics.com/-/media/
article/2019/economic-implications-of-climate-change.pdf.

30. NOAA Office for Coastal Management, "Hurricane Costs,"
2023, https://coast.noaa.gov/states/fast-facts/hurricane-costs
.html/.

31. John Elflein, "Number of Coronavirus Disease 2019
(COVID-19) Deaths in the U.S. as of June 14, 2023, by
Age," Statista, June 14, 2023, https://www.statista.com/
statistics/1191568/reported-deaths-from-covid-by-age-us/.

32. Katie Bach, "New Data Shows Long Covid Is Keeping as Many
as 4 Million People out of Work," Brookings, August 24, 2022,
https://www.brookings.edu/articles/new-data-shows-long-covid
-is-keeping-as-many-as-4-million-people-out-of-work/.

33. Gopi Goda and Evan Soltas, "The Impacts of COVID-19 Illnesses on Workers," NBER Working Paper Series, September 2022, https://www.nber.org/system/files/working_papers/ w30435/w30435.pdf.

34. Rakesh Kochhar and Jesse Bennett, "U.S. Labor Market Inches Back from the COVID-19 Shock, but Recovery Is Far from Complete," Pew Research Center, April 14, 2021, https://www .pewresearch.org/short-reads/2021/04/14/u-s-labor-market -inches-back-from-the-covid-19-shock-but-recovery-is-far-from -complete/.

35. Amy Harder, "How Climate Change Feeds off Itself and Gets Even Worse," *Axios*, August 31, 2020, https://www.axios.com/ 2020/08/31/climate-change-feedback-loops/.

36. Richard Parncutt, "The Human Cost of Anthropogenic Global Warming: Semi-quantitative Prediction and the 1,000-Tonne Rule," *Frontiers in Psychology* 10 (2019), https://doi.org/ 10.3389/fpsyg.2019.02323.

37. U.S. Department of Defense, "Department of Defense Climate Risk Analysis," 2021, https://media.defense.gov/2021/ Oct/21/2002877353/-1/-1/0/DOD-CLIMATE-RISK -ANALYSIS-FINAL.PDF.

38. Luke J. Harrington, Dave Frame, Andrew D. King, and Friederike E. L. Otto, "How Uneven Are Changes to Impact-Relevant Climate Hazards in a 1.5 °C World and Beyond?" *Geophysical Research Letters* 45, no. 3 (2018): 6672–6680.

39. Susanne C. Moser and Lisa Dilling, eds., *Creating a Climate for Change* (Cambridge: Cambridge University Press, 2007), 344.

40. Kim Stanley Robinson, "The Coronavirus Is Rewriting Our Imaginations," *New Yorker*, May 1, 2020, https://www .newyorker.com/culture/annals-of-inquiry/the-coronavirus -and-our-future/.

41. Arbib and Seba, *Rethinking Humanity*, 40.

42. Leslie Paul Thiele, *Sustainability*, 2nd ed. (New York: Polity, 2016), 149.

CHAPTER 2

1. Torrey Podmajersky, *Strategic Writing for UX: Drive Engagement, Conversion, and Retention with Every Word* (Sebastopol, CA: O'Reilly Media, 2019), 11.

2. Google, "Ten Things We Know to Be True," accessed April 18, 2024, https://about.google/philosophy/.

3. Podmajersky, *Strategic Writing*, 37.

4. Russell Willerton, *Plain Language and Ethical Action: A Dialogic Approach to Technical Content in the 21st Century* (New York: Routledge, 2015), 173.

5. Rahel Anne Bailie and Noz Urbina, *Content Strategy: Connecting the Dots between Business, Brand, and Benefits* (Denver, CO: XML Press, 2012), 81.

6. Chip and Dan Heath, *Made to Stick: Why Some Ideas Survive and Others Die* (New York: Random House, 2007), 262.

7. Liz Herman, "Identity Disruption and the Technical Communicator," *Intercom Magazine*, May–June 2020, https://www.stc.org/intercom/2020/08/identity-disruption-and-the-technical-communicator/.

8. World Economic Forum, "A New Paradigm for Business of Data," July 2020, https://www3.weforum.org/docs/WEF_New_Paradigm_for_Business_of_Data_Report_2020.pdf.

9. David Dylan Thomas, *Design for Cognitive Bias* (New York: A Book Apart, 2020), 15.

10. Janice Redish, *Letting Go of the Words: Writing Web Content That Works* (Cambridge, MA: Morgan Kaufmann, 2012).

11. Gini Martinez, "Why Conducting UX Research Is Essential for Product and Content Usability," *Intercom*, November–December 2022, https://www.stc.org/intercom/2022/11/why-conducting-ux-research-is-essential-for-product-and-content-usability/.

12. Kara Pernice, "F-Shaped Pattern of Reading on the Web: Misunderstood, but Still Relevant (Even on Mobile)," Nielsen Norman Group, November 12, 2017, https://www.nngroup.com/articles/f-shaped-pattern-reading-web-content/.

13. Redish, *Letting Go of the Words*, 94.

14. Christopher Balmford, "Getting the Structure Right: Process, Paradigm, and Persistence (Part 2)," *Clarity* 43 (1999): 14–22.

15. Sarah Winters, *Content Design* (London: Content Design London, 2017), 2.

16. Rachel Lovinger, "Content Strategy: The Philosophy of Data," *Boxes and Arrows*, March 27, 2007, https://boxesandarrows.com/content-strategy-the-philosophy-of-data/.

17. Willerton, *Plain Language*, 86.

18. Plain Language Action and Information Network, "What Is Plain Language?" accessed April 18, 2024, https://www.plainlanguage.gov/about/definitions/.

19. Willerton, *Plain Language*, 59.

20. Winters, *Content Design*, 37.

21. Plain Language Action and Information Network, "Federal Plain language Guidelines," accessed April 18, 2024, https://www.plainlanguage.gov/guidelines/.

22. Podmajersky, *Strategic Writing*, 119.

23. Winters, *Content Design*, 41.

24. Willerton, *Plain Language*, 29.

25. MailChimp, "Ease Cognitive Overload in UX Design," accessed May 20, 2024, https://mailchimp.com/resources/cognitive-overload.

26. Tom Greenwood, *Sustainable Web Design* (New York: A Book Apart, 2021), 22.

27. "Page Weight," *Web Almanac*, September 26, 2022, https://almanac.httparchive.org/en/2022/page-weight/.

CHAPTER 3

1. Sustainable Web Design, "Estimating Digital Emissions," November 28, 2023, https://sustainablewebdesign.org/calculating-digital-emissions/.

2. SINTEF, "Big Data, for Better or Worse: 90% of World's Data Generated over Last Two Years," *ScienceDaily*, May 22, 2013, https://www.sciencedaily.com/releases/2013/05/130522085217.htm/.

3. Lin Taylor, "Climate Change: Is Video Streaming Pushing Up Harmful Emissions?" World Economic Forum, June 16, 2021, https://www.weforum.org/agenda/2021/06/coronavirus-pandemic-streaming-video-calls-data-environment-emissions/.

4. U.S. Energy Information Administration, "U.S. Energy Facts Explained," August 16, 2023, https://www.eia.gov/energyexplained/us-energy-facts/.

5. Mister Mobility, "Why iOS Apps Are Significantly Larger Than Android Apps: Explained," *Mobility Arena*, January 5, 2020, https://mobilityarena.com/ios-apps-are-larger-than-android-apps/.

6. Statista, "Number of Monthly Active Instagram Users from January 2013 to December 2021," December 2021, https://www.statista.com/statistics/253577/number-of-monthly-active-instagram-users/.

7. Stefan Larson, "Venmo Networth, Revenue Valuation and Stats, 2024," January 19, 2024, https://prioridata.com/data/venmo-statistics/.

8. Statista, "Monthly Number of Uber's Active Users Worldwide from 2017 to 2023, by Quarter," February 2024, https://www.statista.com/statistics/833743/us-users-ride-sharing-services/.

9. Heinz Tschabitscher, "Why Are Email Files So Large?" *Lifewire*, June 7, 2021, https://www.lifewire.com/what-is-the-average-size-of-an-email-message-1171208/.

10. "The World's Real-Time Billionaires," *Forbes*, accessed June 8, 2024, https://www.forbes.com/real-time-billionaires/#5bfcd93a3d78/.

11. "Ethereum Energy Consumption Index," *Digiconomist*, accessed April 18, 2024, https://digiconomist.net/ethereum-energy-consumption/.

12. Renee Obringer, Benjamin Rachunok, Debora Maia-Silva, Maryam Arbabzadeh, Roshanak Nateghi, and Kaveh Madani, "The Overlooked Environmental Footprint of Increasing Internet Use," *Resources, Conservation and Recycling* 167 (April 2021), https://doi.org/10.1016/j.resconrec.2020.105389.

13. "Video Filesize Calculator," *Tool Stud*, https://toolstud.io/video/filesize.php.

14. Discover Pods, "The Podcast Trends Report," 2019, https://discoverpods.com/wp-content/uploads/2019/09/The-Podcast-Trends-Report-2019-1.pdf.

15. Kendall Breitman, "Podcast Statistics and Trends (and Why They Matter)," Riverside, March 30, 2024, https://riverside.fm/blog/podcast-statistics/.

16. Blubrry, "Mp3 (MPEG Layer 3) Tips for Podcasting," accessed June 7, 2024, https://blubrry.com/manual/creating-podcast-media/audio/mp3-mpeg-layer-3-tips/.

17. Gerry McGovern publishes his research related to *World Wide Waste* and his forthcoming book on his blog *Insights*. See https://gerrymcgovern.com/new-thinking.

18. Giovanni Andrés Quintana-Pedraza, Sara Cristina Vieira-Agudelo, and Nicolás Muñoz-Galeano, "A Cradle-to-Grave Multi-pronged Methodology to Obtain the Carbon Footprint of Electro-intensive Power Electronic Products," *Energies* 12, no. 17 (2019), https://doi.org/10.3390/en12173347.

19. Priyanka Shrestha, "Brits' 'Thank You' Emails Have a Massive Carbon Footprint," *Energy Live News*, November 27, 2019, https://www.energylivenews.com/2019/11/27/brits-thank-you-emails-have-a-massive-carbon-footprint/.

CHAPTER 4

1. Lynn H. Kaack, Priya L. Donti, Emma Strubell, George Kamiya, Felix Creutzig, and David Rolnick, "Aligning Artificial Intelligence with Climate Change Mitigation," *Nature Climate Change* 12 (2023): 518–527.

2. Francesca Rodriguez Sawaya, "Storytelling as Connection: Building Better Relationships with Users in Content Design," Button Conference, October 16–19, 2023.

3. Mariarosaria Taddeo, Andreas Tsamados, Josh Cowls, and Luciano Floridi, "Artificial Intelligence and the Climate Emergency: Opportunities, Challenges, and Recommendations," *One Earth* 4, no. 6 (2021): 776–779, https://doi.org/10.1016/j.oneear.2021.05.018.

4. Amy L. Stein, "Artificial Intelligence and Climate Change," *Yale Journal on Regulation* 37, no. 3 (2020), https://www .yalejreg.com/print/artificial-intelligence-and-climate-change/.

5. Roberto Verdecchia, June Sallou, and Luís Cruz, "A Systematic Review of Green AI," *WIREs Data Mining and Knowledge Discovery* 13, no. 4 (July–August 2023), https://doi.org/ 10.1002/widm.1507.

6. Kimberly Steele, "AI and Cloud Adoption Propel Data Center Demand to Record Levels for 2023," JLL, August 24, 2023, https://www.us.jll.com/en/newsroom/ ai-and-cloud-adoption-propel-data-center-demand-in-2023/.

7. Verdecchia, Sallou, and Cruz, "A Systematic Review."

8. Stein, "Artificial Intelligence."

9. Taddeo et al., "Artificial Intelligence."

10. Alex de Vries, "The Growing Energy Footprint of Artificial Intelligence," *Joule* 7, no. 10 (2023): 2191–2194.

11. Dylan Patel and Afzal Ahmad, "The Inference Cost of Search Disruption—Large Language Model Cost Analysis," *SemiAnalysis*, February 9, 2023, https://www.semianalysis .com/p/the-inference-cost-of-search-disruption/.

12. David Patterson, Joseph Gonzalez, Urs Hölzl, Quoc Le, Chen Liang, Lluis-Miquel Munguia, Daniel Rothchild, et al., "The Carbon Footprint of Machine Learning Training Will Plateau, Then Shrink," *Computer* 55, no. 7 (July 2022): 18–28.

13. Monika Zalnieriute and Tatiana Cutts, "How AI and New Technologies Reinforce Systemic Racism," submission to the Study on Patterns, Policies and Processes Leading Racial Discrimination and on Advancing Racial Justice and Equality for the 54th Session of the United Nations Human Rights Council, October 3, 2022, https://www.ohchr.org/sites/default/files/documents/hrbodies/hrcouncil/advisorycommittee/study-advancement-racial-justice/2022-10-26/HRC-Adv-comm-Racial-Justice-zalnieriute-cutts.pdf.

14. Gina Lazaro, "Understanding Gender and Racial Bias in AI," *Harvard Social Impact Review*, May 17, 2022, https://www.sir.advancedleadership.harvard.edu/articles/understanding-gender-and-racial-bias-in-ai/.

15. Billy Perrigo, "Exclusive: OpenAI Used Kenyan Workers on Less Than $2 per Hour to Make ChatGPT Less Toxic," *Time*, January 18, 2023, https://time.com/6247678/openai-chatgpt-kenya-workers/.

16. Zachary B. Wolf, "AI Can Be Racist, Sexist and Creepy: What Should We Do about It?" CNN, March 18, 2023, https://www.cnn.com/2023/03/18/politics/ai-chatgpt-racist-what-matters/index.html/.

17. Victor Galaz, Miguel A. Centeno, Peter W. Callahan, Amar Causevic, Thayer Patterson, Irina Brass, Seth Baum, et al., "Artificial Intelligence, Systemic Risks, and Sustainability," *Technology in Society* 67 (November 2021), https://doi.org/10.1016/j.techsoc.2021.101741.

18. Alex Reisner, "These 183,000 Books Are Fueling the Biggest Fight in Publishing and Tech," *The Atlantic*, September 25, 2023, https://www.theatlantic.com/technology/archive/2023/09/books3-database-generative-ai-training-copyright-infringement/675363/.

19. Stein, "Artificial Intelligence."

20. Sunder Ali Khowaja, Parus Khuwaja, Kapal Dev, Weizheng Wang, and Lewis Nkenyereye, "ChatGPT Needs SPADE (Sustainability, PrivAcy, Digital Divide, and Ethics) Evaluation: A Review," *ArXiv*, April 13, 2023, https://doi.org/10.48550/arXiv.2305.03123.

21. Myeongjun Erik Jang and Thomas Lukasiewicz, "Consistency Analysis of ChatGPT," *ArXiv*, March 11, 2023, https://doi.org/10.48550/arXiv.2303.06273.

22. Charlotte Freitag, Mike Berners-Lee, Kelly Widdicks, Bran Knowles, Gordon S. Blair, and Adrian Friday, "The Real Climate and Transformative Impact of ICT: A Critique of Estimates, Trends, and Regulations," *Patterns* 2, no. 9 (2021), https://doi.org/10.1016/j.patter.2021.100340; Jeff Overton, "The Growth in Greenhouse Gas Emissions from Commercial Aviation," Environmental and Energy Study Institute, June 9, 2022, https://www.eesi.org/papers/view/fact-sheet-the-growth -in-greenhouse-gas-emissions-from-commercial-aviation/.

23. Toke Haunstrup Christensen, Ruth Mourik, Sylvia Breukers, Tomas Mathijsen, and Herjen van den Heuve, "Young People, ICT and Energy—Status and Trends in Young People's Use and Understanding of ICT and Energy Consumption," Aalborg University, 2014, https://vbn.aau.dk/ws/portalfiles/portal/201886616/UseITsmartly_WP2_report_D2.1_FINAL.pdf.

24. David Patterson, Joseph Gonzales, Quoc Le, Chen Liang, Lluis-Miquel Munguia, Daniel Rothchild, David So, Maud Texier, and Jeff Dean, "Carbon Emissions and Large Neural Network Training," *ArXiv*, April 21, 2021, https://doi.org/10.48550/arXiv.2104.10350.

25. See https://gerrymcgovern.com/new-thinking.

26. Chris Stokel-Walker, "The Generative AI Race Has a Dirty Secret," *Wired*, February 10, 2023, https://www.wired.com/story/the-generative-ai-search-race-has-a-dirty-secret/.

CHAPTER 5

1. John Elkington, "25 Years Ago I Coined the Phrase 'Triple Bottom Line': Here's Why It's Time to Rethink It," *Harvard Business Review*, June 25, 2018, https://hbr.org/2018/06/25-years-ago-i-coined-the-phrase-triple-bottom-line-heres-why-im-giving-up-on-it/.

2. Erika Hall, "Thinking in Triplicate," *Medium*, July 16, 2018, https://medium.com/mule-design/a-three-part-plan-to-save-the-world-98653a20a12f/.

3. Charles Conn, "Patagonia Chair: 'We Are Turning Capitalism on Its Head by Making the Earth Our Only Shareholder,'" *Yahoo! Finance*, September 14, 2022, https://finance.yahoo.com/news/patagonia-chair-turning-capitalism-head-204019814.html/.

4. Larry Fink, "Larry Fink's 2020 Letter to CEOs: A Fundamental Reshaping of Finance," BlackRock, 2020, https://www.blackrock.com/corporate/investor-relations/2020-larry-fink-ceo-letter/.

5. ADV Ratings, "World's Top Asset Management Firms," accessed April 18, 2024, https://www.advratings.com/top-asset-management-firms/.

6. Scott Anthony, "Kodak's Downfall Wasn't about Technology," *Harvard Business Review*, July 15, 2016, https://hbr.org/2016/07/kodaks-downfall-wasnt-about-technology/.

7. Steve Orr, "Genesee River Cleanup Proposed to Remove Kodak's Toxic Silver Legacy," *Democrat and Chronicle*, October 4, 2019, https://www.democratandchronicle.com/story/news/2019/10/04/genesee-river-cleanup-kodaks-silver-pollution-rochester-ny/3856185002/.

8. United States Environmental Protection Agency, "Case Summary: Bankruptcy Settlements Reached with the Eastman Kodak Company Worth $49 Million," May 13, 2014, https://www.epa.gov/enforcement/case-summary-bankruptcy-settlements-reached-eastman-kodak-company-worth-49-million/.

9. Deloitte, "A Call for Accountability and Action: The Deloitte Global 2021 Millennial and Gen Z Study," 2021, https://www.deloitte.com/content/dam/assets-shared/legacy/docs/insights/2022/2021-deloitte-global-millennial-survey-report.pdf.

10. John Davies, "State of the Profession," GreenBiz Group, 2020, https://info.greenbiz.com/rs/211-NJY-165/images/State_of_the_Profession_2020_Report.pdf.

11. Patrick Flynn, "Why Corporate Sustainability Must Change," Salesforce, January 23, 2020, https://www.salesforce.com/news/stories/why-corporate-sustainability-must-change/.

12. Sammy Spiegel, "How Salesforce Fosters Sustainability as a Culture—Not Just a Department," Salesforce, September 14, 2022, https://www.salesforce.com/news/stories/salesforce-sustainability-jobs/.

13. Ryan Jenkins, "Talent Acquisition insights for Recruiting Gen Z with Ana Recio," *Next Generation Catalyst Podcast*, episode 110, accessed June 7, 2024, https://blog.ryan-jenkins.com/talent-acquisition-insights-for-recruiting-gen-z-with-ana-recio/.

14. Davies, "State of the Profession."

15. World Economic Forum, "These 79 CEOs Believe in Global Climate Action," November 23, 2015, https://www.weforum.org/agenda/2015/11/open-letter-from-ceos-to-world-leaders-urging-climate-action/.

16. Marguerite Ward, "More Than 200 CEOs from Companies Like Microsoft, Walmart, and JP Morgan Unveil a New Plan to Address Racism in America," *Business Insider*, October 15, 2020, https://www.businessinsider.com/business-roundtable-plan-advance-racial-equity-jpmorgan-walmart-microsoft-2020-10/.

17. Salesforce, "Marc and Lynne Benioff, Salesforce Announce $300 Million in Investments to Accelerate Ecosystem Restoration and Climate Justice," October 28, 2021, https://www.salesforce.com/news/press-releases/2021/10/28/marc-and-lynne-benioff-and-salesforce-announce-investment-to-accelerate-ecosystem-restoration-and-climate-justice/; Kerry A Dolan, "Salesforce Billionaire Marc Benioff Pledges $200 Million for Reforestation, Climate Entrepreneurs," *Forbes*, October 28, 2021, https://www.forbes.com/sites/kerryadolan/2021/10/28/salesforce-billionaire-marc-benioff-pledges-200-million-for-reforestation-climate-entrepreneurs/?sh=22bc807a5cd0/.

18. Aaron K. Chatterji and Michael W. Toffel, "The New CEO Activists: A Playbook for Polarized Political Times," *Harvard Business Review*, January–February 2018, https://hbr.org/2018/01/the-new-ceo-activists/.

19. Sammy Spiegel, "A New 'Environmental Capitalism' Is Needed: Benioff and Other Salesforce Execs Speak at Davos," Salesforce, May 25, 2022, https://www.salesforce.com/news/stories/salesforce-davos-2022/.

20. Rose Ors, "Voices in Sustainability: An Interview with Amy Weaver," Berkeley Law, April 24, 2023, https://www.law.berkeley.edu/research/business/berkeley-laws-institute-business

-society/events/voices-in-sustainability-an-interview-with-amy
-weaver/.

21. David Norman, "The Role of Business in Education
for Sustainable Development," Business Fights Poverty,
October 24, 2018, https://businessfightspoverty.org/
the-role-of-business-in-eduction-for-sustainable-development/.

22. James Arbib and Tony Seba, *Rethinking Humanity: Five
Foundational Sector Disruptions, the Lifecycle of Civilizations,
and the Coming Age of Freedom* (RethinkX, 2020), 55.

23. Paul Polman and C. B. Bhattacharya, "Engaging Employees
to Create a Sustainable Business," *Stanford Social
Innovation Review*, Fall 2016, https://ssir.org/articles/entry/
engaging_employees_to_create_a_sustainable_business/.

24. Jeff Greene, "PepsiCo Foundation Partners with WaterAid
India to Promote Sustainable Access to Clean Water and
Sanitation Facilities in West Bengal," WaterAid, May 31, 2022,
https://www.wateraid.org/us/media/pepsico-foundation
-partners-wateraid-india-clean-water/.

25. Deloitte, "The Sustainable Consumer, 2023," 2023, https://
www2.deloitte.com/uk/en/pages/consumer-business/articles/
sustainable-consumer.html/.

26. World Small Business for Sustainable Development, "CEO
Guide to the Sustainable Development Goals," March 2017,
https://docs.wbcsd.org/2017/03/CEO_Guide_to_the_SDGs/
English.pdf.

27. Michael Copley, Esther Whieldon, and Robert Clark, "ESG
Funds Remain Relative Safe Havens in Coronavirus Downturn,"
S&P Global Market Intelligence, May 19, 2020, https://www
.spglobal.com/marketintelligence/en/news-insights/latest-news

-headlines/esg-funds-remain-relative-safe-havens-in-coronavirus
-downturn-58679570/.

28. John Hale, "Despite the Downturn, U.S. Sustainable Funds
Notch a Record Quarter for Flows," Morningstar, April 9, 2020,
https://www.morningstar.com/sustainable-investing/despite
-downturn-us-sustainable-funds-notch-record-quarter-flows/.

29. Fink, "Larry Fink's 2020 Letter."

30. Hale, "Despite the Downturn."

31. Nuveen, "Responsible Investing's Role in Risk Mitigation,"
January 30, 2023, https://www.nuveen.com/en-us/insights/
responsible-investing/seventh-annual-responsible-investing
-survey/.

32. Bloomberg, "Global ESG Assets Predicted to Hit $40 Trillion by
2030, Despite Challenging Environment, Forecasts Bloomberg
Intelligence," February 8, 2024, https://www.bloomberg.com/
company/press/global-esg-assets-predicted-to-hit-40-trillion-by
-2030-despite-challenging-environment-forecasts-bloomberg
-intelligence/.

33. Morgan Stanley, "Sustainable Funds Outperformed Peers,
2023," February 29, 2024, https://www.morganstanley.com/
ideas/sustainable-funds-performance-2023-full-year/.

34. Copley, Whieldon, and Clark, "ESG Funds Remain."

35. Davies, "State of the Profession."

36. BlackRock, "Sustainability Reporting: Convergence to
Accelerate Progress," October 2020, https://www.blackrock
.com/corporate/literature/publication/blk-commentary
-sustainability-reporting-convergence.pdf.

37. Mike Atherton and Carrie Hane, *Designing Connected Content*
(Indianapolis, IN: New Riders, 2017), 132.

CHAPTER 6

1. J. A. Devlin-Hegedus, F. McGain, R. D. Harris, and J. D. Sherman, "Action Guidance for Addressing Pollution from Inhalational Anaesthetics," *Anaesthesia* 77, no. 9 (2022): 1023–1029.

2. Relly Annett-Baker, "What Is the Value of Content Design," Button Conference keynote speech, October 2022.

3. This Is Content Design, "The Content Design Manifesto," May 13, 2024, https://thisiscontent.design/.

4. U.S. Bureau of Labor Statistics, "Employer Costs for Employee Compensation Summary," March 13, 2024, https://www.bls.gov/news.release/ecec.nr0.html/.

5. "Using Page Speed in Mobile Search Ranking," *Google Search Central Blog*, January 17, 2018, https://developers.google.com/search/blog/2018/01/using-page-speed-in-mobile-search/.

6. "Seconds to Snag or Lose Shoppers," *Chicago Tribune*, September 11, 2009, https://www.chicagotribune.com/2009/09/11/seconds-to-snag-or-lose-shoppers/.

7. Akamai, "Online Retail Best Practices: How Web and Mobile Performance Optimize Conversion and User Experience," May 2019, https://www.akamai.com/site/en/documents/white-paper/how-web-and-mobile-performance-optimize-conversion-and-user-experience-white-paper.pdf.

8. Amy Gallo, "The Value of Keeping the Right Customers," *Harvard Business Review*, October 29, 2014, https://hbr.org/2014/10/the-value-of-keeping-the-right-customers/.

9. CallMiner, "New Research Finds Not Valuing Customers Leads to $136 Billion Switching Epidemic," September 27, 2018, https://callminer.com/news/press-releases/new-research-finds-not-valuing-customers-leads-to-136-billion-switching-epidemic/.

Notes

10. "#WellActually, Americans Say Customer Service Is Better Than Ever," *Business Wire*, December 15, 2017, https:// www.businesswire.com/news/home/20171215005416/en/ WellActually-Americans-Say-Customer-Service-is-Better -Than-Ever/.

11. Rich Hein, "Customer Retention Strategies for Driving Loyalty in Uncertain Times," *CMS Wire*, February 21, 2023, https:// www.cmswire.com/customer-experience/customer-retention -strategies-for-driving-loyalty-in-uncertain-times/.

12. Kahlid Saleh, "Customer Acquisition vs. Retention Costs— Statistics and Trends," Invesp, February 23, 2015, https://www .invespcro.com/blog/customer-acquisition-retention/.

13. Blake Morgan, "50 Stats That Prove the Value of Customer Experience," *Forbes*, September 24, 2019, https://www.forbes .com/sites/blakemorgan/2019/09/24/50-stats-that-prove-the -value-of-customer-experience/?sh=1b47156d4ef2/.

14. Shep Hyken, "Ninety-Six Percent of Customers Will Leave You for Bad Customer Service," *Forbes*, July 12, 2020, https://www .forbes.com/sites/shephyken/2020/07/12/ninety-six-percent-of -customers-will-leave-you-for-bad-customer-service/ ?sh=2ad27f6c30f8/.

CHAPTER 7

1. Melissa Bailey, "How Journalists Can Address Mistrust in Pandemic Coverage and Help 'Flatten the Curve,'" Nieman Reports, August 5, 2020, https://niemanreports.org/articles/ how-journalists-can-address-mistrust-in-pandemic-coverage -and-help-flatten-the-curve/.

2. Angel E. Navidad, "Stanford Marshmallow Test Experiment," *Simply Psychology*, https://www.simplypsychology.org/marshmallow-test.html/.

3. Peter Morville, *Intertwingled: Information Changes Everything* (Ann Arbor, MI: Semantic Studios, 2014), 2.

4. Morville, *Intertwingled*, 2.

5. Robert Jay Lifton, "Beyond Psychic Numbing: A Call to Awareness," *American Journal of Orthopsychiatry* 52, no. 4 (1982): 619–629.

6. Brian Resnick, "A Psychologist Explains the Limits of Human Compassion," *Vox*, September 5, 2017, https://www.vox.com/explainers/2017/7/19/15925506/psychic-numbing-paul-slovic-apathy/.

7. Brenda Voorthuis, "The Effect of Individual-Level vs. Group-Level Perspective Taking on Prosocial Behaviour," bachelor's thesis, University of Twente, February–June 2017, https://essay.utwente.nl/72616/1/Voortuis_BA_BMS.pdf.

8. Paul Slovic, "'If I Look at the Mass I Will Never Act': Psychic Numbing and Genocide," *Judgment and Decision Making* 2, no. 2 (April 2007), https://doi.org/10.1017/S1930297500000061.

9. Madeline Bell, "Tenlee's Story: Thriving after a Heart Transplant," *Breaking Through with Madeline Bell*, March 31, 2023, https://breakingthrough.podbean.com/e/tenlee-s-story-thriving-after-a-heart-transplant/.

10. World Wildlife Fund, "Troubling News for Monarch Butterfly Populations," March 21, 2023, https://www.worldwildlife.org/stories/troubling-news-for-monarch-butterfly-populations/.

11. UNHCR, "Famine Explained: Definition, Causes and Facts," April 4, 2023, https://www.unrefugees.org/news/famine-explained-definition-causes-and-facts/.

12. David Dylan Thomas, *Design for Cognitive Bias* (New York: A Book Apart, 2020), 4.

13. Fino Menezes, "All It Took to Clean Up This Beach Was a Fish Sculpture Called 'Goby,'" *Bright Vibes*, June 5, 2018, https://www.brightvibes.com/all-it-took-to-clean-up-this-beach-was-a-fish-sculpture-called-goby/.

14. Nathaniel Geiger, Karen Gasper, Janet K. Swim, and John Fraser, "Untangling the Components of Hope: Increasing Pathways (Not Agency) Explains the Success of an Intervention that Increases Educators' Climate Change Discussions," *Journal of Environmental Psychology* 66 (December 2019), https://doi.org/10.1016/j.jenvp.2019.101366.

15. Yale Program on Climate Change Communication, "Global Warming's Six Americas," accessed April 10, 2024, https://climatecommunication.yale.edu/about/projects/global-warmings-six-americas/.

16. Yale Program on Climate Change Communication, "Global Warming's Six Americas."

17. Natalie Kobayashi, "American Climate Perspectives Survey, 2019, Vol. III," Eco America, March 13, 2019, https://ecoamerica.org/american-climate-perspectives-survey-2019-vol-iii/.

18. Geiger et al., "Untangling the Components."

19. Annette Simmons, *The Story Factor: Inspiration, Influence, and Persuasion through the Art of Storytelling* (New York: Basic Books, 2019), 3.

20. Brendan Nyhan and Jason Reifler, "Misinformation and Fact-Checking: Research Findings from Social Science," New America Foundation, February 2012, https://www.issuelab.org/resources/15316/15316.pdf.

21. Lauren Phipps, "The Role of Innovation in Changing Behavior towards a Circular Economy," GreenBiz webinar, recorded November 12, 2020, https://www.greenbiz.com/webcast/role-innovation-changing-behavior-towards-circular-economy/.

22. Simmons, *The Story Factor*, xiv.

23. Geiger et al., "Untangling the Components."

24. Liese Coulter, Anne Coudrain, and Silvia Serrao-Neumann, eds., *Communicating Climate Change Information for Decision-Making* (New York: Springer Climate, 2018), 94.

25. Mark Hertsgaard, "Climate-Justice Stories in Every Community, Waiting to Be Told," *Columbia Journalism Review*, June 17, 2020, https://www.cjr.org/covering_climate_now/climate-justice-george-floyd.php/.

26. "Talking Shop: Climate Change and Racial Justice," *Covering Climate Now*, June 14, 2020, https://youtu.be/p2INFJHvu8g?si=I5E0uP-cqIDvtIW4/.

27. Aumyo Hassan and Sarah J. Barber, "The Effects of Repetition Frequency on the Illusory Truth Effect," *Cognitive Research Principles and Implications* 6 (2021), https://doi.org/10.1186/s41235-021-00301-5.

28. Nyhan and Reifler, "Misinformation and Fact-Checking."

29. Chip and Dan Heath, *Made to Stick: Why Some Ideas Survive and Others Die* (New York: Random House, 2007), 246.

30. Morville, *Intertwingled*, 11.

31. John Fraser, Victor Pantesco, Karen Plemons, Rupanwita Gupta, and Shelley J. Rank, "Sustaining the Conservationist," *Ecopsychology* 5, no. 2 (2013), https://doi.org/10.1089/eco.2012.0076.

Notes

32. Margaret Robertson, *Communicating Sustainability* (London: Routledge, 2019), 24.

33. Heath, *Made to Stick.*

APPENDIX A

1. United Nations Department of Economic and Social Affairs for Sustainable Development, "The 17 Goals," accessed May 14, 2024, https://sdgs.un.org/goals/.

APPENDIX B

1. Michal Bednarski, "What Is the Greenhouse Effect?" NRDC, June 5, 2023, https://www.nrdc.org/stories/greenhouse-effect -101#whatis/.

2. Michal Bednarski, "What Are Greenhouse Gases?" NRDC, June 5, 2023, https://www.nrdc.org/stories/greenhouse-effect -101#gases/.

3. Bednarski, "What Are Greenhouse Gases?"

4. Environmental Investigation Agency, "What Are Hydroflurocarbons?" accessed May 14, 2024, https://us.eia.org/ campaigns/climate/what-are-hydrofluorocarbons/; Kerstin Wyssusek, Ka Lo Chan, Gerard Eames, and Yasmin Whately, "Greenhouse Gas Reduction in Anaesthesia Practice: A Departmental Environmental Strategy," *BMJ Open Quality* 11, no. 3 (2022), https://doi.org/10.1136/bmjoq-2022-001867.

5. United States Environmental Protection Agency, "Overview of Greenhouse Gases," April 11, 2024, https://www.epa.gov/ ghgemissions/overview-greenhouse-gases/.

6. United States Environmental Protection Agency, "Sulfur Hexafluoride (SF6) Basics," April 1, 2024, https://www.epa.gov/eps-partnership/sulfur-hexafluoride-sf6-basics/.

7. Hannah Ritchie, Max Roser, and Pablo Rosado, "Renewable Energy: Renewable Energy Sources Are Growing Quickly and Will Play a Vital Role in Tackling Climate Change," Our World in Data, January 2024, https://ourworldindata.org/renewable-energy/.

8. Hannah Ritchie, Max Roser, and Pablo Rosado, "Energy Production and Consumption: Explore Data on How Energy Production and Use Varies across the World," Our World in Data, January 2024, https://ourworldindata.org/energy-production-consumption/.

9. Gerry McGovern, *World Wide Waste: How Digital Is Killing Our Planet—and What We Can Do about It* (Gormanston, Ireland: Silver Beach, 2020), 22.

APPENDIX C

1. Philip Shabecoff, "Global Warming Has Begun, Expert Tells Senate," *New York Times*, June 24, 1988, https://www.nytimes.com/1988/06/24/us/global-warming-has-begun-expert-tells-senate.html/.

2. Hoesung Lee, Katherine Calvin, Dipak Dasgupta, Gerhard Krinner, Aditi Mukherji, Peter Thorne, Christopher Trisos, et al., "Synthesis Report of the IPCC Sixth Assessment Report (AR6): Summary for Policymakers," 2023, https://report.ipcc.ch/ar6syr/pdf/IPCC_AR6_SYR_SPM.pdf.

Glossary

IF YOU HAVE AN INTEREST in going deeper into the world of sustainability or find yourself working with the sustainability department, you'll discover a seemingly impenetrable rabbit hole of acronyms, jargon, and concepts with conflicting names.

I try to avoid jargon throughout the book, but this glossary should give you some basic terms that will help you understand what you hear when working in the sustainability space or talking with upper management.

1.5: This refers to the goal of keeping planetary warming to 1.5°C beyond preindustrial levels. We've already reached 1°C, and it's believed that we're increasing at a rate of 0.2°C with each decade. Without dramatic interventions in reducing greenhouse gas emissions, we will be on track to see warming of 2.5°C or more.

Alternative energy: Energy that does not come from fossil fuels. See also **green energy** or **renewables**.

Anthropogenic: This refers to the influence of human beings on nature. It is derived from the ancient Greek *ánthrōpos*, meaning "human," and *genic*, meaning "caused by."

Blackwater: Contaminated wastewater that needs to be drained from buildings using separate pipes.

Cap and trade: Refers to a "cap" on emissions and the ability of organizations to "trade" carbon credits. Also known as emissions trading.

Carbon credit: Carbon credits are permits that organizations buy to allow them to emit a fixed amount of greenhouse gas emissions. One carbon credit equals one ton of carbon dioxide or its equivalent. While this doesn't reduce carbon emissions directly, it does make emissions more costly. The idea is to incentivize organizations to seek lower-cost, more-sustainable alternatives. These permits can be sold or traded.

Carbon footprint: The greenhouse gas emissions generated by an individual or organization.

Carbon negative: When an organization goes beyond **net zero** and removes additional carbon dioxide from the atmosphere. See also **climate positive**.

Carbon neutral: When an organization says they are carbon neutral, they mean that whatever carbon emissions they generate are offset by an equivalent amount of carbon being removed. This can be achieved by purchasing carbon offsets elsewhere. It is not the same as **net zero**.

Carbon offsets: This is the act of reducing or removing greenhouse gas emissions in one area to compensate for emissions generated elsewhere. By buying carbon credits, an organization can claim to be carbon neutral with no changes to its business model.

Carbon positive: Some organizations use "carbon positive" as a marketing term to explain **carbon negative** and **climate positive**, but it becomes incredibly confusing for the audience to understand. It's best to avoid this terminology.

CDP: The Carbon Disclosure Project is a nonprofit that gathers data and content for a centralized repository for climate reporting.

Circularity: This can also be known as the circular economy. In a circular economy, we are able to reduce our consumption by reusing as much as we can and recycling existing materials into new products. This can also be referred to as "cradle to cradle" in contrast with "cradle to grave," where products are disposed of at the end of their useful life.

Climate change: In a changing climate, there are long-term shifts in temperatures and weather patterns. While there have been natural shifts during the history of the planet, the term specifically refers to anthropogenic climate change, the human-induced change that has rapidly occurred since the onset of the Industrial Revolution.

Climate crisis: This is a more accurate term for what's happening to our climate. Also referred to as climate disaster or climate catastrophe.

Climate positive: This is when an organization goes beyond **net zero** and removes additional carbon dioxide from the atmosphere. See also **carbon negative**.

Climate readiness: You become climate ready by taking action that protects the economy and infrastructure to safeguard health, safety, and quality of life within a given population. Many groups have climate readiness plans in place, from local communities to major international **NGOs**.

CO_2: Carbon dioxide. Carbon dioxide emissions do occur naturally on Earth, but there has been an acceleration in those emissions from the burning of fossil fuels. Carbon dioxide is the baseline gas by which other greenhouse gas emissions are measured; it's not uncommon to see "___ tons of CO_2 equivalent (CO_2e)."

CO_2e: As you can see in Appendix B, different greenhouse gases have different levels of global warming potential. Carbon dioxide (CO_2) is the standard for measurement. CO_2e is calculated by multiplying the amount of gas by its **global warming potential**. Example: Methane has a GWP of 25; 1 kg of methane emissions has a CO_2e of 25 kg.

Conscious capitalism: This refers to a free-market economy that benefits both consumers and the environment.

CSR: Corporate social responsibility programs integrate social causes into the business model or employee culture.

Decarbonization: We achieve this by phasing out greenhouse gas emissions from industries without compromising competitiveness and prosperity.

Environmental justice: Environmental justice movements strive to protect poor and marginalized communities from harm associated with hazardous waste or resource extraction.

ESG: Environmental, social, and governance (ESG) reporting is how organizations document the risks and opportunities they face, measured through a sustainability lens. Critics say that ESG is more about how the outside world affects an organization (limited natural resources, supply chain challenges, and so on) than how the organization affects the outside world. In reality, it goes both ways. If a company notes that they're facing risks with fresh water supply in a drought-stressed community or energy availability in a region with grid instability, they will need to look for alternative and more sustainable ways of doing business in the future.

ESG investing: This is the act of explicitly applying environmental, social, and governance (ESG) criteria to the process of selecting investments.

ETF: As part of the Paris Agreement, countries established an enhanced transparency framework (ETF). Starting in 2024, countries will report transparently on their progress toward climate change mitigation and adaptation measures. This is similar in concept to ESG reporting but at a national level.

Externalities: These are costs or benefits that are not directly felt by the actor—either an individual or organization. A new factory may bring positive externalities of jobs and money to the local economy while simultaneously bringing the negative externality of watershed pollution.

Fair trade: We can provide better prices and decent working conditions in the developing world through improvements to social and environmental standards.

Global warming: In the past, climate change was referred to as global warming. This seemed logical because the planet is, in fact, warming overall. However, much of the public assumed that it meant the weather would be consistently warmer, and the presence of prolonged cold snaps (polar vortex) actually fed into the perception that scientists were wrong. A warming planet will experience instability and more severe weather events and extreme temperatures at both ends of the spectrum.

Global warming potential (GWP): This refers to the effects that a particular gas will cause over a period of 100 years after emissions. Carbon dioxide has a GWP of 1. Other greenhouse gases have higher impacts, with sulfur hexafluoride (SF_6) leading the pack with a GWP of 25,200.

Governance: There are similar but different meanings for content and ESG reporting. "Content governance" talks about the processes for creating, publishing, and maintaining content. "Sustainability governance" refers to how a company is run: structure, internal controls, and accountability.

Green energy: See **renewables**.

Greenhouse gases (GHG): There are six primary gases that absorb radiant energy from the sun and trap that heat in the atmosphere. They can remain in the atmosphere for anything from a few weeks to thousands of years.

Greenwashing: This is when companies use marketing spins to make a product or organization seem more sustainable and environmentally friendly. A notable example is Volkswagen's "clean diesel" marketing, when the company was actually fitting vehicles with override software to only appear clean during emissions testing. The company paid millions in fines as a result.

Greywater: When wastewater doesn't include toxic chemicals, it can be reused. Water from sinks and showers, for example, can be reused for landscape irrigation, preserving the available fresh water.

GRI: The Global Reporting Initiative is an international organization that sets standards for reporting material impacts across the 17 Sustainable Development Goals (**SDGs**) set forth by the United Nations.

IPCC: The Intergovernmental Panel on Climate Change was created by the United Nations to provide scientific assessments of the risks and impacts of a changing climate and make suggestions for mitigating impacts and disruptions.

Just transition: I mean "just" as in "morally right and fair," not "barely/only." A just transition protects workers' rights and livelihoods as the marketplace shifts from an extractive economy to a sustainable one.

LEED: A worldwide green building certification program. An acronym for Leadership in Energy and Environmental Design.

Lightweighting: We can swap traditional materials for lighter materials or reduce the amount of material used. It is commonly heard in terms of reducing the weight of packaging material.

Logistics: This is the transportation and storage of goods and services from their point of origin to their final destination. Also known as "business logistics." It plays an important role in supply chain management.

Materiality: In accounting, this is the principle that items are reasonably likely to have an impact on investors' decision-making. In sustainability circles, it refers not only to ESG issues that the company can affect but also to those that it may be affected by (e.g., Does the company affect the fresh water supply of the local environment, or does the availability of fresh water in a drought-stressed ecosystem affect the company's operations?).

Natural capital: These are the resources we have on Earth, such as soil, air, water, and living things.

Natural resources: These are things that occur in nature and are used for financial gain. Forests, minerals, water, and agricultural land are all natural resources.

Net zero: There are two types of net zero: net zero carbon (carbon emissions only) and net zero (considers all greenhouse gas emissions). Net zero requires an organization to cut all types of greenhouse gas emissions through energy efficiency, use of renewables, or other reductive approaches. No greenhouse gases are emitted. This differs from **carbon neutral**.

NGO: Nongovernmental organizations are typically nonprofits working in the social sciences or humanitarian fields. Some examples include Médecins Sans Frontières (Doctors without Borders) or World Central Kitchen.

Paris Agreement: This is a legally binding international treaty on climate change. It was adopted by 196 parties in 2015 with the goal of limiting global warming to 1.5°C. To achieve this, we must begin reducing greenhouse gas emissions immediately.

Physical risks: The impacts to society and the economy are often caused by extreme weather or natural disasters.

Renewables: Also known as renewable energy, this refers to energy drawn from resources that are naturally replenished, such as solar, wind, water, and geothermal heat. It's sometimes referred to as "green energy."

Resilience: This is the measure of how well an organization or community is prepared for disruptive events. These could be caused by sudden disasters (tornadoes, hurricanes, wildfires) or longer-term risks (rising temperatures, famine, drought).

Rolling coal: Some people will commit the antienvironmental practice of modifying a diesel truck engine to actively emit as much sooty exhaust as possible. These modifications are a violation of the federal Clean Air Act, as well as specific laws in some states.

SBTi: The Science Based Targets initiative is a collaboration between CDP, the United Nations Global Compact, World Resources Institute, and the World Wide Fund for Nature. It defines and promotes best practices for emissions reductions and **net zero** targets in line with the **Paris Agreement**.

Scope 1/2/3 emissions: There are three types of emissions that are measured in ESG reporting: Scope 1: Direct emissions generated by an organization's facilities or vehicles. Scope 2: Indirect emissions from the electricity, heating, steam, or cooling purchased by an organization. Scope 3: Everything else. This includes upstream emissions and waste from purchased goods and services in the supply chain, business travel, and employee commutes; it also includes downstream emissions and waste from distribution, processing, end-of-life, leased assets, and franchises.

SDGs: The Sustainable Development Goals "provide a shared blueprint for peace and prosperity for people and the planet, now and into the future." Developed by the United Nations, the 17 goals address the interconnectedness of social, health, economic, and environmental considerations.

Stakeholders: This is the "people" category of the triple bottom line. Stakeholders are all people involved in or affected by an organization—employees, communities, people in the supply chain, customers, and future generations—and not simply shareholders or prospective investors.

Supply chain: This encompasses everything in the systems leading up to an item's manufacture. This can include individuals (labor), raw materials, manufactured components, technology, transportation, and warehousing.

Sustainability: We must meet our present needs without depleting resources for the future. If we live sustainably, future generations will have the ability and resources to meet their needs as well.

Sustainable development: The balancing of environmental concerns and economic development.

TCFD: The Task Force on Climate-Related Financial Disclosures focuses on the disclosure of the financial impacts of ESG risks.

Threat multiplier: This term is used to explain how climate change will accelerate existing instabilities and worsen other issues like health, inequality, poverty, and hunger.

Triple bottom line: Businesses that focus on the triple bottom line assign equal weight to people, the planet, and profits. Balancing social, environmental, and financial outcomes helps businesses to be more resilient. The term was coined by author and entrepreneur John Elkington in 1994 in an effort to provoke deeper thinking about capitalism and its future.

Resources

TECHNOLOGY AND WASTE

- *World Wide Waste: How Digital Is Killing Our Planet—and What We Can Do about It*, by Gerry McGovern
- *Sustainable Web Design*, by Tom Greenwood
- Website Carbon Calculator: WebsiteCarbon.com

SUSTAINABILITY COMMUNICATIONS

- *Creating a Climate for Change: Communicating Climate Change and Facilitating Social Change*, edited by Susanne C. Moser and Lisa Dilling
- *Communicating Sustainability*, by Margaret Robertson
- *Communicating Climate Change Information for Decision-Making*, edited by Silvia Serrao-Neumann, Anne Coudrain, and Liese Coulter

LEAVING "BUSINESS AS USUAL" BEHIND

- *Sustainability*, by Leslie Paul Thiele
- *The Ecology of Commerce*, by Paul Hawken
- *Natural Capitalism: Creating the Next Industrial Revolution*, by Paul Hawken, Amory Lovins, and L. Hunter Lovins
- GreenBiz newsletters: GreenBiz.com

HOPE IN THE FACE OF CLIMATE CRISIS

- *All We Can Save*, edited by Ayana Elizabeth Johnson and Katharine K. Wilkinson
- *The Story of More: How We Got to Climate Change and Where We Go from Here*, by Hope Jahren

COMMUNICATIONS BEST PRACTICES

- *Content Strategy for the Web*, by Kristina Halvorson and Melissa Rach
- *Content Design*, by Sarah Richards
- *Just Enough Research*, by Erika Hall
- *Plain Language and Ethical Action*, by Russell Willerton
- Plain Language Action and Information Network: PlainLanguage.gov

- Scriptorium Business Case Calculator: https://www
  .scriptorium.com/2024/02/estimate-your-roi-for
  -content-operations-with-our-calculator

THE PSYCHOLOGY OF BIAS AND CHANGE

- *Design for Cognitive Bias*, by David Dylan Thomas
- "Solution Aversion: On the Relation Between Ideology
  and Motivated Disbelief," by Troy H Campbell and
  Aaron C. Kay
- "Untangling the Components of Hope: Increasing
  Pathways (Not Agency) Explains the Success of an
  Intervention That Increases Educators' Climate Change
  Discussions," by Nathaniel Geiger, Karen Gasper,
  Janet K. Swim, and John Fraser
- "Risk as Feelings," by G. F. Loewenstein, E. U. Weber,
  C. K. Hsee, and N. Welch

Index

bias
confirmation, 158–160
interpretation, 98
related to AI, 97–98
transfer context, 98
BlackRock Capital, 108, 117,
120–121
blackwater, 105
blockchain, 70–71
Books3 dataset, 98
BP (formerly British Petroleum), 26
breaking down walls of words, 45–46
Breker, Melissa, 81
Business Fights Poverty, 114
business resilience, 116–118
business value of content, 148–150.
See also capitalist case for sustainability; corporations
impact of, on customers, 139–144
operational benefits, 144–148
trusting in content strategy,
137–139

C

California, "Orange Day" in, 24–25
call center, avoiding, 146
"A Call for Accountability and
Action" (Deloitte), 109
cap and trade (emissions trading),
106
capitalist case for sustainability
building ESG capability, 121–129
ESG reporting, 118–121
overview of, 29–35, 103–104
serving all stakeholders, 106–109
staking claim, 129–130
success through differentiation,
114–118
sustainability as recruiting tool,
109–113
triple bottom line, 104–106
carbon credits, 106

carbon dioxide (CO_2), 183
Carbon Disclosure Project (CDP), 26
carbon footprint
of apps, 64–67
of artificial intelligence, 92–96,
99–100
of audio and video, 72–81
and data as energy, 60–63
defined, 218
of devices, 82–86
of digital data, 1–3, 59–60, 64, 186
of email, 67–68
of NFTs, 68–70
as shifting emphasis to personal
responsibility, 26
"Carbon Majors Report" (CDP), 26
carbon mitigation, capitalist case for.
See capitalist case for sustainability; sustainability
carbon neutrality, 106
CDP (Carbon Disclosure Project), 26
CEO activism, 111–112
"CEO Guide to the Sustainable
Development Goals"
(WBCSD), 115–116
change, leverage for, 26–27, 35–36.
See also positive change, driving
channels, content strategy across,
41–43
ChatGPT, 91, 95, 98, 99
Chatterji, Aaron, 112
CH_4 (methane), 183
Chouinard, Yvon, 107
circularity, 119, 126
"Circumstances Affecting the Heat of
Sun's Rays" (Foote), 188
clear content. *See* content strategy
climate change
and affect heuristics, 157
as affecting everyone everywhere,
24
and capitalist case for carbon
mitigation, 30–33

Index

increased focus on sustainability
by, 16–17
responsibility for sustainability,
24–29, 35–36, 64
serving all stakeholders, 106–109
success through differentiation,
114–118
sustainability as recruiting tool for,
109–113
triple bottom line, 104–106
costs
human, 132–137
of load times, 140–142
of not trusting in content strategy,
138–139
CO_2 (carbon dioxide), 183
Coulter, Liese, 168
COVID-19 pandemic
and always-on culture, 85
and awareness of need for sustainability, 14–15, 19–21, 31
effect of, on workforce health,
32–33
global internet traffic during, 64
Crary, Jonathan, 59
create once, publish everywhere
(COPE), 145–146
Creating a Climate for Change (Moser
and Dilling), 13
cryptocurrencies, 70
CSR (corporate social responsibility),
111
customers
as central stakeholder group, 107
impact of sustainable content on,
139–144
increased focus on sustainability by
consumers, 16–17
operational benefits of sustainable
content, 144–148
cutting content, 43–44

D

dark data, 5–6
data. *See* digital data
data centers, 5–6, 92–93
data-heavy pages, 52–55, 139–140.
See also content strategy
Davies, John, 120
decarbonization, 16, 19, 114
delayed gratification, 152
Deloitte, 109, 115
design, content. *See* content strategy
Design for Cognitive Bias (Thomas),
43, 156
Design for Safety (PenzeyMoog), 6
Designing Connected Content
(Atherton and Hane), 123
devices, carbon footprint of, 82–86
de Vries, Alex, 95
diet, sustainable, 27, 28, 29
differentiation, success through,
114–118, 127–128
digital data. *See also* artificial intelligence; carbon footprint;
content audits; content strategy;
sustainable content
best practices in creation of, 7–9
emissions impact of removing,
59–60, 61
as energy, 2–3, 60–63
moving, 7
storage of, 5–6
sustainable content connection,
3–5
thinking before creating, 86–87
Dilling, Lisa, 13
discharge papers, lack of plain language in, 48–49
discrimination related to AI, 97–98
disinformation, strong positive connections combating, 169–170
download speed, 140–142, 144

Index

E

Earth Overshoot Day, 33–34
economic incentives for sustainability,
    114–118. *See also* capitalist case
    for sustainability
economy built on extraction and
    exploitation, 34–35
Ecopsychology, 170–171
eco-wakening, 20
education, lack of interdisciplinary
    thinking in, 13
electric vehicles (EVs), 27, 28, 29
electronic devices, carbon footprint
    of, 82–86
Elkington, John, 105–106
email
    carbon cost of, 67–68, 69, 85
    cost of not trusting content strat-
        egy, 138
emissions. *See also* carbon footprint
    from AI, 92–96, 99–100
    from app downloads and use,
        65–67
    atmospheric, 17–18
    from audio and video, 72–81
    from corporate emails, 67–68
    cost of not trusting content strat-
        egy, 138–139
    and data as energy, 60–63
    from devices, 82–86
    impact of removing digital con-
        tent, 59–60, 61
    leaner pages, 53–56
    from NFTs, 68–70
    produced by digital data, 1–3
    scope 3, 121
empathy, psychic numbing as erod-
    ing, 154–155
employees
    as central stakeholder group, 107
    human cost of content, 132–137
    sustainability as recruiting tool for,
        109–113

energy
    and artificial intelligence, 92–96,
        99–100
    data as, 2–3, 60–63
    renewables, 184–186
    required to move data, 7
    rising consumption of, 185–186
    solar, 27, 29
    sources of, 183–186
    used by devices, 83–84
enhanced transparency framework
    (ETF), 188
environmental impacts, increasing
    focus on, 15–17
environmental justice, 168
Environmental Protection Agency
    (EPA), 63
environmental, social, and gover-
    nance (ESG) capability
    assigning actions, 128–129
    content analysis, 125–128
    content inventory, 124–125
    flagging for sustainability, 128
    overview of, 121–123
    staking claim, 129–130
    sustainability-focused content
        audit, 123–124
environmental, social, and gov-
    ernance (ESG) investing,
    116–118
environmental, social, and gov-
    ernance (ESG) reporting,
    118–121
ETF (enhanced transparency frame-
    work), 188
Ethereum blockchain, 70–71
ethical challenges related to AI,
    96–99
EVs (electric vehicles), 27, 28, 29
externalities, 36, 105, 116, 153
external market forces, 114–116

Index

hope
  communicating sustainability based on, 163–164
  related to sustainability, 19
household solar energy, 27, 29
human cost of content, 132–137
hydrofluorocarbons (HFCs), 184

I

ideas, as similar to viruses, 165–167
"Identity Disruption and the Technical Communicator" (Herman), 42
illusory truth effect, 169
images
  in content strategy, 46–47
  leaner pages, 52–56
  and load times, 140–141
  role of, in plain language, 51–52
immediate gratification, 152
individual responsibility for sustainability, 23–29
inequalities, systemic, 20–21
inference in AI, 91–92, 95–96
Inflation Reduction Act of 2022, 19
Instagram, 65, 66
institutional investors, sustainability as attracting, 112–113
interdisciplinary thinking, need for, 12–15
Intergovernmental Panel on Climate Change (IPCC), 21, 24, 31, 188
internal champion, finding, 172
International Energy Agency, 26
interpretation bias, 98
Intertwingled (Morville), 152, 170
intuition, 156–158
inverted pyramid style, writing in, 44–45
investment funds based on ESG criteria, 116–118

investors, sustainability as attracting, 112–113
IPCC (Intergovernmental Panel on Climate Change), 21, 24, 31, 188
iPhone apps, 65–66

J

Jang, Myeongjun Erik, 99
The Joe Rogan Experience podcast, 79, 80
just transition, 19

K

key point, starting with, 44–45
Kodak, 108–109
Krenn, Susan, 151–152
Kyoto Protocol, 188

L

labor force, climate change and, 31–33
Landek, Matt, 92–93
language, plain
  and compliance, 147–148
  in content strategy, 47–52
large language model (LLM), 91
leaner pages, need for, 52–56
Letting Go of the Words (Redish), 43
leverage for change at work, 26–27, 35–36, 64
Lifton, Robert Jay, 154
lightweighting, 224
listening to audience, 171–172
LLM (large language model), 91
load times, 139–142, 144
logistics, 224
long COVID, 32
Lovinger, Rachel, 49

Index

Index

About the Author

ALISA BONSIGNORE is the founder of Clarifying Complex Ideas, which develops award-winning sustainable content strategies for global clients. Her pioneering metrics have helped organizations measure and mitigate the carbon footprint of their digital information. Alisa's clients have avoided tons of scope 3 greenhouse gas emissions that contribute to climate change. She is a fellow of the Society for Technical Communication, a Certified Master Gardener specializing in xeriscaping, and a keynote speaker who is taller than she looks on Zoom.